SUSAN ELLIOT WRIGHT

ALL
YOU
EVER
WANTED

**SIMON &
SCHUSTER**

London · New York · Sydney · Toronto · New Delhi

First published in Great Britain by Simon & Schuster UK Ltd, 2022

Copyright © Susan Elliot Wright, 2022

The right of Susan Elliot Wright to be identified as author of
this work has been asserted in accordance with the
Copyright, Designs and Patents Act, 1988.

3 5 7 9 10 8 6 4

Simon & Schuster UK Ltd
1st Floor
222 Gray's Inn Road
London WC1X 8HB

Simon & Schuster Australia, Sydney
Simon & Schuster India, New Delhi

www.simonandschuster.co.uk
www.simonandschuster.com.au
www.simonandschuster.co.in

A CIP catalogue record for this book
is available from the British Library

Paperback ISBN: 978-1-3985-0330-4
eBook ISBN: 978-1-3985-0331-1
Audio ISBN: 978-1-3985-1621-2

Typeset in Bembo by M Rules
Printed and bound by CPI Group (UK) Ltd, Croydon, CR0 4YY

MIX
Paper | Supporting
responsible forestry
FSC® C171272

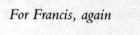

For Francis, again

'Probably.' He glances at his watch.

He's in work mode now, his head already at school, already focused on the first of the many meetings he seems to have to attend as an assistant head.

'Right, I have *got* to go.' He takes hold of Bonnie's bare foot, lifts it to his mouth and blows a raspberry against her skin, sending her into paroxysms of giggles. He opens the front door, waves and is gone.

Bonnie's still waving as Simon's car pulls away. Her bottom lip is wobbling, so I distract her with my biggest *isn't-everything-fun* smile. 'Come on, Bonnie-bon. Shall we get you ready to go to Gemma's, eh?'

She's caught halfway between protest and compliance, then I see my words register. Bonnie knows what *going to Gemma's* means. It means other children to play with, guinea pigs to feed and a soft-ball pit that would rival the one in IKEA. Her little mouth twitches into a smile and she nods emphatically. 'Deh,' she says, which at thirteen months is as near as she can get to *yes*.

There's still plenty of time. If I can be away from Gemma's by eight, I should be at school by quarter past, which'll give me a good half hour before my meeting with Sarah. This time last year, we were both heads of department, so I didn't feel quite so vulnerable. To Sarah's credit, she hasn't used her seniority against me; at least, not so far. Though who could blame her if she did? Maybe she's just biding her time.

Bonnie is mercifully cooperative, and I soon have her changed and her bag packed ready for the day. With her sitting on my hip, I shake some granola into a bowl and add a spoonful of yoghurt, then slip a pod into the coffee machine and press the button. I mustn't be complacent – when I'm running late, minutes can whizz by in seconds.

Bonnie kicks her legs, indicating she's had enough of being held, so I set her down on the oak-panelled floor and she immediately starts shuffling along on her bottom to get to her toybox. While she's occupied, I go through into the utility room, feeling a pang of sadness as I refill Oscar's water bowl and set it back down, just in case. Then I load the washing machine and switch it on. I should have done this yesterday when I was at home, but what with Bonnie's one-year check, then toddler yoga, then shopping, it went right out of my head.

I manage to eat my breakfast and drink my coffee while Bonnie is taking things out of the toybox, and it's still only twenty-five to eight. If I follow this routine every morning, things should be okay. Having set off the dishwasher, I sling my rucksack and Bonnie's bag over my shoulder, grab my phone and then hoist Bonnie onto my hip. 'Shall we go see Gemma?'

Bonnie nods. 'Deh.'

But before I've taken another step, I see a large puddle of water creeping out of the utility room and into the kitchen. 'Shit!' I say aloud, making Bonnie look at me, startled. I dump my stuff on the table and run to turn the washing machine off, then I chuck down the stack of clean towels that are folded on the shelves ready to go upstairs. They go some way to mopping up the water, but more is leaking out. I look at the clock — 7.54, no, 7.55. I don't have time to deal with this now. With one hand, because I don't want to put Bonnie down on the wet tiles, I empty what's left in the laundry basket over the floor. It'll have to wait until I get home.

I gather up my bags again, set the burglar alarm and, murmuring to Bonnie to reassure her, strap her into her car seat. If nothing else goes wrong, I'll still be on time. *Please, please don't let there be too much traffic.* As I pull out of the drive, I instinctively scan the hedges and front gardens in vain for a glimpse of grey-and-white fur.

Gemma opens the door before I reach it. 'Morning!' She reaches behind her head to pull her long yellow-blonde hair into a ponytail with one of the hairbands she keeps around her wrist. 'I was beginning to think you weren't coming.'

'Washing machine's on the blink — leaking all over the bloody floor.' I catch Gemma's disapproving look at the same time as I spot three-year-old twins Ava and Isla hovering in the hallway. 'Oops, sorry.' Gemma is strict about what she calls 'foul language' in front of the children. She takes Bonnie from my arms and plants a huge kiss on her cheek. 'Hello, darling,' she says, and is rewarded with a toothy grin. She turns back into the house. 'Did you get it sorted?' she says over her shoulder as she ushers the twins into the knocked-through sitting room she's converted into a giant playroom.

'No, I'll have to call a plumber. I hope they'll come out tonight.'

'What's wrong with it?'

'No idea. I wouldn't have a clue what to look for. I'm not very practical, to be honest. Nor is Simon. Best to get someone in.'

'That'll cost an arm and a leg.' Gemma shrugs. 'Still, you probably don't mind.'

I'm not sure how to take that. I suspect Gemma thinks we're ridiculously wealthy. We're not hard up, but we're not exactly rich, and now my salary has plummeted, we're nowhere near as comfortable as we were a year ago.

'Sorry, I've got to run – there's her bag. She didn't sleep well so she might be a bit grouchy.'

Gemma kisses Bonnie on the nose. 'She won't be grouchy with her Auntie Gemma, will she? Eh? No, she won't.' Another kiss. 'We're going to have fun, aren't we, poppet? Eh? Bye-bye, Mummy.' She waves Bonnie's hand at me. 'Bye-bye.'

Bonnie looks perfectly happy to be left. I feel a slight pang that my daughter doesn't seem to miss me. I'm glad she's settled so well and I'd be mortified if she were to cry, but she never has, apart from the very first day. In fact, she seems more than happy to be with Gemma. *Stop it,* I tell myself.

My meeting's in fourteen minutes, but the roads aren't busy and I'm making good time. When my phone rings, I barely glance at the screen as I hit *answer*. 'Hello,' I say on speakerphone.

'Oh, hello,' says a hesitant female voice. 'Are you … I mean, I saw a poster … Have you lost a little grey cat?'

'Yes! Yes, we have! Have you seen him? Is he all right?'

'He's fine. He's here in my flat, eating a tin of tuna. He's been hanging around for a few days, and then I saw your poster so I thought I'd better bring him in and call you.'

'Oh, my goodness, that's wonderful news! Thank you so much. Shall I—'

'Where do you live? I'm out and about today, so I can bring him round.'

'I'm ... thank you, but ...' I glance at the clock. I've literally got five minutes to get to school, get parked and get to the third floor. 'I'm just on my way to work. Oh God, I know this sounds terrible, but I've got this really important meeting. I don't suppose you could look after him until—'

'No problem. I'll hang onto him until you finish work.'

'No, that's really kind of you, but I can pick him up at lunchtime.'

'Honestly, it's no problem at all, and he's such a gorgeous cat – I wouldn't mind his company for a few hours. What time do you get home? Let me have your address and I'll bring him round then. I'm Anna, by the way.'

'No, it's fine. I don't want to put you out. I should be free by—'

'It'd be more convenient if I could drop him off later,' she says, her tone slightly impatient. There's a pause and then she adds, 'Sorry, it's just that it's all a bit mad here at the moment. There's roadworks down my road and you can't park and ... it really would be easier for me if I could drop him off later.'

'Well, if you're absolutely sure it's no trouble.'

I give her the address.

CHAPTER THREE

Once I've found somewhere to park, I have two minutes to get to Sarah's office, and as I run into the building I can feel the sweat prickling under my arms. The lift doors are closing but I just manage to slip through and press the button for the third floor, then I lean against the side to get my breath back before checking my appearance in the mirror. A bit ruffled, but not too bad. The lift pings and as the doors open, I straighten my uncomfortably tight dress, take a deep breath and stride along the corridor to Sarah's office. We managed to avoid each other for much of the time before I went on maternity leave, but now she, like Simon, is an assistant head and, thanks to the last round of staff cuts, she's also my line manager.

'Good morning,' she greets me with a curt nod, gesturing to a chair.

At this proximity, I'm reminded how attractive she is. Not pretty, exactly, but sexy, and in that sort of innocent way that suggests it's natural, that she doesn't even have to try. She's done her hair in one of those clever four-strand plaits, and the pale caramel colour looks great with her olive skin, as does the simple khaki shift she's wearing. She looks stunning, and it occurs to me that Simon will have already seen her this morning because now they're part of the Senior Leadership Team, they'll have both been at the eight o'clock meeting.

'As I'm sure you're aware,' she's saying, 'the SLT has been focusing on a timekeeping drive for several weeks, and all reports need to be with the head by the end of the spring term, which is why I scheduled this meeting for today. As you know, this is not a formal disciplinary interview, more a ...' Her eyes slide away to the left as she hesitates, and I wonder if she'd been going to say *friendly*.

'Look,' I interrupt, 'this is awkward and embarrassing for both of us. Well, at least, *I* feel embarrassed. There's no reason you should.'

She looks at me for a second. 'Thank you for that, at least.'

'Sarah, I—'

'Anyway,' she cuts in. Her voice is brisk, perhaps because she's irritated or maybe it's simply an indication that she wants to move on. 'Let's keep this professional,' she says, and that's exactly what she is: supremely, perfectly, untouchably professional. She runs through the three occasions on which I've been late for first period, talks about the procedure should this happen again, and acknowledges that on one of those occasions, there was a major traffic problem following a burst water main, resulting in four other teachers being late. As I

23

listen, I can't help wondering if beneath that efficient, professional veneer, she's mentally punching the air. I wouldn't blame her for feeling smug. But her face betrays nothing. If anything, she looks calm; serene, almost. Her make-up is artfully applied as always and perfectly intact, whereas I'm fairly sure I'll already have mascara smudges under my eyes. When I first met Sarah, I thought she looked plain and frumpy, but she'd only just lost her dad, having been away from school for much of the term helping her mum to look after him in his final weeks, so it was no wonder she looked rough. It still makes me cringe to think of the pain I must have caused her at what was already such an awful time. And if I'd known about her dad before? Would that have made any difference? I realise she's looking at me. 'Sorry,' I say. 'I missed that.'

'Well, it's nice to know I have your full attention.'

'Sorry, Sarah, I . . .' I look down into my lap, wishing, as the saying goes, that the ground would open up and swallow me. I raise my head and look her in the eye. 'I'm sorry,' I say again. 'No excuses. It's hard to concentrate when you're curling up with shame and embarrassment. Please, carry on, I'm listening properly now.'

Sarah pauses as though weighing up the genuineness of my response, and then she continues, her voice possibly stronger and even more confident than before. I nod and agree. Yes, I need to be more organised, no, I won't let this happen again, yes, I understand that if there's a next time, it'll be a formal disciplinary interview, and no, I don't think three days a week is too much for me while Bonnie is small. I'm momentarily surprised that she knows Bonnie's name. Simon must have told her.

'And if it *does* become a disciplinary matter, you're entitled to have someone with you at the meeting – either your union rep or another colleague.' Sarah looks up at the clock, then back at me. 'Is there anything else you'd like to say?'

I wait a moment before replying. 'No, thank you. Only that I can assure you it won't happen again, not unless there's a dire emergency or something. It's taken me a while to get it into my head that I need to allow twice as much extra time as I did before Bon ... before I had a baby.' I don't like her knowing Bonnie's name, and by saying it, it feels like I'm complicit in allowing her an intimacy with our family.

Sarah nods, then stands, gesturing towards the door. I take a breath. 'Okay, I'm going to just say this.' I almost lose my nerve. 'Look, I know "sorry" doesn't cut it—'

'Not really, no.'

'But I am. I'm very sorry for causing you so much pain.'

Sarah doesn't look at me, but she pauses, her hand on the doorknob. I'm tempted to abandon my little speech and run out of the room, but I don't. 'I don't expect you to forgive me, or to be more than civil to me, but thank you for not using this as an opportunity to make me even more uncomfortable than I already am.' When I stop speaking, the silence in the room is particularly noticeable. Outside, kids are hurrying along the corridor on their way to first period. She looks at me for a moment, then, with another curt nod, opens the door and thanks me for coming.

When Simon finally told me he was engaged, I was more concerned about his betrayal of me than his more reprehensible betrayal of Sarah. I was devastated, but even once I'd got over the initial shock, I hadn't ended it, had I?

Simon had made a point of talking to me in the staff room on my first day at Woodview. I was sitting there, wondering if I'd done the right thing in taking a post at a school in one of the most deprived areas in south-east London when he came over and introduced himself, looking right into my eyes as he shook my hand. I'd never seen eyes that were such a dark blue, almost navy, and I felt this incredible warmth when he smiled. He said it was a great place to work and he was sure I'd be happy there. He was so welcoming and reassuring that I relaxed immediately.

Once we'd got together, he was attentive and affectionate, two things I'd craved for a long time. It felt like he *knew* me, knew who I was in a way I didn't – still don't – know myself. When we were together, he seemed focused entirely and absolutely on me, and it never even crossed my mind that he was thinking of anything or anyone other than me. That's why I was so shocked when he told me about Sarah. 'How come you were so relaxed when we went out?' I asked him. 'Weren't you worried someone from school would see us and tell Sarah?'

He shook his head, then ran his hand through his hair. He looked miserable, eaten up with guilt now it was out in the open. 'No, I didn't. Not for a moment. I guess if I *had*, that would make me even more of a shit, because it would mean I knew exactly what I was doing, that I was deceiving her deliberately, but I wasn't. I know it sounds unbelievable, but ...' he looked around helplessly, as though searching for the words, '... I was so intoxicated by you, so *absorbed* with you ...' His hand went through his hair again. 'I couldn't think about anything else. It was like I'd forgotten Sarah existed.' He glanced up at me and must have seen the incredulity on my face. 'I know, I know,' he said. 'It makes me sound like a complete and utter bastard.'

I shrugged, but I was secretly flattered and thrilled to know he was so besotted with me.

'I was so incredibly attracted to you. You sort of blotted out everything else.' His voice cracked, and I felt a momentary panic that his guilt was so great that he'd change his mind, say this was all a big mistake and go running back to try and make it up with Sarah. But then he reached for me, placed his hands on my upper arms and looked deeply into my eyes. 'I know this is right, Emily. I *know* it. I didn't want to hurt Sarah, of course I didn't. She's an amazing woman. But I should have ended it with her before. It was good while it lasted, but we want different things, Sarah and me.'

'So why did you get engaged?'

'She hadn't told me she didn't want kids. And when the subject came up, I couldn't say, "well, that's it, it's over", could I? I needed to think, decide if there was any way we could make it work. But being a dad's important to me. I'm not saying I want a family immediately but I've always assumed I'd be a father one day.'

'I get that,' I murmured. 'I've always known I wanted to be a mum.'

He took both my hands in his. 'That's why I know this is right. You and me, we want the same things.' Then he sighed. 'But before I had a chance to talk to Sarah about it, she got the call from her mum to say her dad was dying, so I couldn't say anything then, could I? Then I met you, and it was too late. I was in love with you and I couldn't do anything about it.'

I loved that he said *in love*.

A few weeks into our relationship, he'd got a call from Sarah. He said it was the first time they'd spoken in weeks because reception in Northumberland was so bad. But she was calling from a payphone in the hospital to say her dad had died. She didn't expect Simon to travel up for the funeral, but she wanted to let him know she'd be home in a few days. It was only then that he told me he was engaged. I thought for a moment it was some sort of silly joke, and then I saw the truth on his face.

He waited until she got back to tell her about me. She took it reasonably well, he told me. *Dignified* was the word he used.

'I know I've been a total shit to Sarah, but I'm in love with you now, and there's nothing I can do to change that.' His hands were cupping my face, his eyes searching, then his lips met mine. I returned his kiss more passionately than I intended to. I was still trying to hold back a little, still finding it hard to believe that he could have pushed Sarah so far to the back of his mind that he was able to forget her completely. Yet part of me couldn't help being horribly but deliciously thrilled by the idea that this hot man had fallen for me so powerfully that he felt helpless, unable to do anything about it.

As I'm recalling all this, another memory slithers in, cold and black. I'm walking along the school corridor, a week or so after Sarah returned to school, and I see her coming towards me. I know who she is, obviously, but we've never spoken. My stomach does a somersault and I'm wondering what on earth to say to her when, as she draws near, she leans towards me and hisses, 'Don't think he won't do the same thing to you.'

It's almost five by the time I leave school. One of the new admin women is leaving at the same time, so we exchange pleasantries as we cross the car park. As we get nearer to my car, I notice a cigarette butt squashed out on my bonnet. 'Oh shit,' I say out loud.

The admin woman brushes the fag end off the bonnet, shaking her head. 'I wonder which little toe rag did that?' She pushes her glasses up onto the top of her head, licks the tissue she's taken out of her bag and starts rubbing at the paintwork. 'There,' she says. 'No harm done.'

I lean in to look. It doesn't seem to have left a mark. 'Great,' I say. 'Thanks.'

'I used to work in a car showroom,' the woman says. 'The paintwork's tougher than you think. Dobbing out a fag's not gonna hurt. Anyway,' she gets her car keys out of her pocket, 'this is me.' She points to a red Polo and gives me a wave as she gets into her car.

I smile and return the wave. But I can't help feeling slightly unnerved, as if it's personal. Most of the kids are into vaping now, but some of them still smoke, although they usually hang out behind the old science labs, not in the car park. Maybe I've upset one of them? But it's sanctions that usually piss them off, and I haven't given out any sanctions for weeks.

By the time I've collected Bonnie and am on my way home, it's gone six. I totally forgot to take anything out of the freezer for supper again, but I told the woman who has Oscar I'd be home by six thirty, so there isn't time to stop to pick something up.

My heart sinks when I turn into the drive and see an empty space where Simon's car should be. But I suppose now Oscar's been found, he doesn't need to come home early. I used to stay late myself when I was head of English, but not this often. Do assistant heads really have so much more to do? I find myself thinking again about how gorgeous Sarah looked this morning, and wondering if she's working late as well.

CHAPTER FOUR

I've just poured a glass of wine when, at six thirty on the dot, the doorbell rings. The woman is small, about my height, and maybe a few years older than me. She's wearing jeans and sneakers and a blue hoodie, and she has enormous round, dark eyes that make her quite striking to look at. There's something vaguely familiar about her.

'I'm Anna.' She smiles uncertainly as she holds up a cardboard box, a makeshift cat carrier. She seems nervous. A grey-and-white paw pokes through one of the air holes.

'Oscar!' I grin as I reach for the box. 'Thank you so, so much. Where did you find him?'

'I live over that way.' She turns and waves vaguely up the road. Her darkish-blonde hair hangs down her back in a thick plait. 'I'd seen him sniffing around outside my flat a few times. I noticed him because he's such a lovely colour. Sort of smoky.' Her face relaxes as she hands me the box.

'Funnily enough, my husband suggested Smoky as a name

when we first got him!' I set the box down. 'But I thought he looked rather wild, so we went for Oscar.' The woman doesn't react. I lift Oscar out, closing my eyes and burying my face in his warm fur. He meows loudly, his ears flattened against his head. 'Oh Oscar,' I murmur. 'Where have you been?' But Oscar is unmoved by our reunion so I set him down before he can twist away from me. 'He clearly hasn't missed me as much as I've missed him.'

The woman smiles. 'He's a gorgeous cat.'

'He is, isn't he? Anyway, sorry – come in a sec. I'll get the reward.'

'Oh no.' She shakes her head. 'I don't want the reward. I'm just happy to reunite him with his family.'

'Please, I insist. We're so happy to have him back.'

She drops to a crouching position to stroke Oscar, who's now rubbing his cheek against my shin and purring like a traction engine. 'I'm sure he's pleased too,' she murmurs. 'Beautiful puss.' She straightens up. 'It's very nice of you – you know, the reward and that – but I honestly don't want it. Tell you what, though. Could I be cheeky and ask if you've got a couple of painkillers?' She puts her hand to her creased forehead. 'I've got this shocking headache.'

I notice how thick and dark her eyebrows are, as though she's never plucked them.

'I've had it all day but it's getting worse.'

'Of course! Come through.' I lead the way into the kitchen where Bonnie is happily ensconced in her high-chair, eating quartered strawberries and cubes of mango.

'But I warn you, I'm determined to talk you into taking that reward!'

'No,' the woman says. 'Really, I ...' She puts her hand to her head again and winces, then she appears to sway. 'Sorry, I feel a bit dizzy.'

'Oh gosh, you poor thing. Look, Anna, is it?' I pull out one of the kitchen chairs. 'Have a seat for a minute while I find you some painkillers.'

'Okay, thanks.' She hangs her bag on the back of the chair and sits at the table. 'Hello,' she says to Bonnie. 'What's your name?'

'This is Bonnie ...' I fill a glass with water and take a box of paracetamol from the kitchen cupboard.

'Hello, Bonnie,' Anna says in a baby-friendly voice. 'I'm Anna. What have you got there, then? Ooh, strawberries. Yum yum! Are they nice?'

I smile as Bonnie picks up another strawberry quarter and offers it to Anna.

'Thank you, my darling,' Anna says, 'but I've just had my tea so I'm full up.' She pats her stomach, still beaming at Bonnie, who seems to understand and pushes the strawberry into her own mouth.

I hand the pills and water to Anna. 'There you are. Horrible, those all-day headaches, aren't they?' I notice her hand is trembling slightly as she takes the glass. She looks pale. 'Why don't you just sit here for a bit while they kick in?'

'I might, if you don't mind.' She throws the pills into the back of her mouth and takes a gulp of water, then looks around the room. 'Wow, you've got a sofa in the kitchen! That's amazing. Your whole kitchen is amazing.'

She's looking at the gleaming white cupboards, the polished granite worktops, the hi-spec double oven and induction hob. It *is* an impressive kitchen, and like everything else in this house, it's less than two years old. I've been lucky enough to live in nice houses all my life, as has Simon. Sometimes, I'm reminded that, thanks in part to us both having generous parents, we live a relatively privileged lifestyle.

'It's like something off the telly,' Anna says. 'Those shows where they buy some old dump and then do it up all classy and sell it for like, a million quid or something.'

'We're very lucky.' I smile. 'Have we met before? You look familiar.'

Anna looks right at me. 'Might have.' She pauses, as if she's trying to remember where we might have seen each other, or as if she's waiting for me to remember. Her hand creeps up to the silver locket that hangs around her neck, then she turns back to Bonnie, who's watching her with interest while cramming what's left of the mango into her mouth. 'Lucky to have you, too, aren't they, eh? Because you're a proper cutie, aren't you? Yes, you are!'

The way she talks to Bonnie reminds me of Gemma. Maybe that's what it is. I've always envied Gemma's natural affinity with children, the way she talks to them so easily and unselfconsciously. I struggled with Bonnie at first. It didn't come naturally, but it's much better now. It hits me again, that powerful sense of connection between Bonnie and me. *Flesh of my flesh.* If Bonnie has her own children one day, will chatting to them come naturally to her straightaway, or will she have to work at it like I have?

'And look,' Anna's saying, 'you've almost eaten up all your fruit! What a good girl you are! Fruit is yummy-yum-yums. And it's good for you, isn't it, eh?'

Bonnie rewards her with a wide, mango-stained grin.

'You've made a friend, there!' I glance at the clock. 'Anna, please sit there until you feel better, but you'll have to excuse me for a sec. I've got someone coming to look at my washing machine soon, and I've just remembered I left wet laundry all over the floor.'

'What's up with your machine?' she asks.

'Oh, God knows. I set it this morning and water started pouring out just as I was dashing off to work. Won't be a minute.'

The heap of clothes and towels on the utility room floor are no longer sopping wet, so I scoop them up and shove them back in the laundry basket. Oscar's sitting next to his bowl, tail curled around him, meowing at me for food, as if he'd never been gone. 'All right, Oscar, just a sec.' I tear the top off a pouch of Fishy Feast and squeeze the contents into his dish. He purrs as he eats, and I can hear Bonnie singing a little tune in the kitchen. I turn back to the washing machine and am startled to find Anna standing right behind me.

'Sorry,' she says. 'Did I make you jump?'

'No, no, it's fine. Are you feeling better?'

'Yeah, a bit, thanks. So, a lot of water, was it?'

'Yes! I managed to mop most of it up, but it ran right through into the kitchen.'

'Let's have a look at the back.' She steps towards the machine.

'Oh, there's no need – the man's coming at eight, so—'

'Yeah, but you don't want to pay some bloke if it's something simple, do you?'

'True, but my husband and I are both useless when it comes to things like this.'

Anna smiles. 'Let me have a look, I'm quite good at fixing things.'

'Well, if you're sure . . .'

Anna's already manoeuvring the washing machine out from under the worktop.

'Oh, watch out,' I say as more water splashes out.

'Don't worry.' She bends to look at the back. 'Ah yes.' She straightens up. 'Thought so. Hose has come off. Looks like they didn't do the connector up tight enough and it's worked itself loose.'

'Really? Is that all it is?'

'Yep. Simple as that.' She bends over the machine again. 'So all we need to do . . .' She fiddles around at the back. 'Got a pair of pliers?'

'Er, possibly. I'm not sure.'

'No worries. I should be able to do it by hand.' She furrows those thick brows in concentration, grunts slightly, then straightens up again. 'There. That ought to fix it. But if it starts leaking again, you might need to tighten it a bit more.'

'Thank you so much. I should have had a look myself.' I'm embarrassed now. She must think I'm a complete idiot. We go back through into the kitchen, where Bonnie is doing her best to wriggle out of her highchair. 'Wait a minute, sweet-heart. Mummy'll get you out in a sec.' I grab a couple of baby wipes from the table. 'Anna,' I say as I'm wiping Bonnie's face and hands, 'you are *awesome!* First you find our missing cat, then you repair our washing machine.'

Anna laughs. 'I wouldn't call it a *repair* – it was only a loose connection. Hey, you'd better cancel your repair man or you'll get charged for a call out.'

'Good point!' I unstrap Bonnie and put her down on the floor, where she immediately crawls over to her toybox. 'You've saved my life, you know.' I reach for my phone. 'You are SO going to take that reward money!'

Anna starts to protest again, but before I can insist, the repair man answers. He sounds pissed off but he doesn't charge me, and after I end the call, I go to the drawer in the kitchen where I'd put the five crisp twenty-pound notes in anticipation of Oscar's return. But when I take the money out, Anna holds up her hand and shakes her head. 'I really, seriously don't want your money,' she says quietly. Those huge round eyes are glittering as if she's about to cry.

'Oh gosh, I'm sorry if I've offended you,' I say. 'Are you okay?'

'Sorry,' Anna says in a small voice. 'It's all a bit over-whelming.' Then she blinks and adds, 'It's been quite a day, and I'm just feeling . . .' Then she seems to gather herself. She scrapes her chair back. 'I should get out of your way.'

'No, look, don't rush off. It's been a shitty day for me, too – apart from you bringing Oscar back of course – and I've got a bottle of wine on the go. Why don't you join me? It's only a supermarket Sauvignon, but it does the job.'

'Oh, that would be lovely,' Anna says, her face bright-ening. She looks so delighted you'd think I'd offered her a glass of Bollinger. 'But I probably shouldn't drink alcohol, not with this head.'

I feel an unexpected stab of disappointment. It's been nice having someone here. It's ages since I had a drink with a female friend. My so-called friends seem to have faded away since I had Bonnie, and although I stay in touch with a few of the NCT mums, there's no-one I'm particularly close to. 'Maybe a cup of tea, then? Or coffee?'

'Okay, if you're not too busy. Coffee would be lovely.'

'Great. What would you like? I've got latte, cappuc-cino, mocha?'

'You've got one of those fancy coffee machines!' Anna laughs. 'All right then, if you really don't mind, could I have a cappuccino?'

'Of course.'

'Thanks. You're spoiling me. It's like I'm in Starbucks.'

'It's the least I can do.' I top up my glass while the coffee machine's running, then I take the wine and coffee to the table. 'Cheers,' I say.

'Cheers.' Anna clinks her mug against my glass before taking a sip. 'Ooh, this is lovely! What a treat!'

I look at her as we sit at the huge table by the bay window at the side of the house. I'm tempted to offer the reward again, but maybe that would be patronising. 'So, Anna,' I take a sip, 'how did you learn to fix washing machines? I'm useless at things like that.'

Anna shrugs. 'I suppose I've always had to work out how to fix things when they go wrong. Couldn't afford to get people in. One of my . . . I mean, my mum never had much money so she taught us kids that you should always try and mend stuff if you can.'

'Very sensible. I wish my parents had taught me things like that.'

Anna's hands slide around her coffee mug as though she's trying to warm them.

'What were your parents like, then?' she says. 'Didn't they fix stuff?'

I laugh. 'God, no. It's as much as my mum can do to change a lightbulb. And my dad was a GP. He always said he understood the workings of the human body, so he shouldn't be expected to understand the workings of the Hoover.' Most people smile at that, but Anna leans further forward and says, 'Your mum's still alive then?'

'They both are. I just meant that my dad was a GP before he retired.'

'Oh, I thought you meant he'd passed away.'

'No, he buggered off when I was twelve.' I take another mouthful of wine.

'That's sad,' Anna says. 'It's hard, not having parents around.'

'Yes, I hated it when he left.' I'm about to tell her more but I stop myself. 'Sorry, I talk too much. You don't want to hear my life story.'

Anna smiles. 'I love hearing about people's lives.'

So I carry on. She's a good listener. In fact, she appears to be listening intently, as though what I'm saying is both important and fascinating. I can feel my tongue loosening and the words all backing up, ready to spill out. It feels like a long time since I've had a proper conversation with another woman, other than my mum, and those aren't exactly meaningful conversations, given the things I'm not allowed to mention. There's something about this woman that makes me want to talk. But, I remind myself, she's only here because she was kind enough to bring Oscar back and unlucky enough to have a headache. 'How's your head?' I ask. 'Any better?'

'I think so.' She nods and takes another mouthful of coffee.

I hear the front door shut and the sound of Simon's keys landing in the wooden bowl we keep by the front door. 'Hello!' he shouts.

Bonnie, who has been feeding shapes into her shape sorter, stops what she's doing and whisks her head round to look at me. Then she draws in a breath and widens her eyes. 'Da!' she says.

I glance at the clock. Ten past seven. 'Yes, sweetie, Daddy's home.'

'Traffic was a bloody nightmare,' he says before he's even in the room. 'Thought I'd never get home.'

'Da!' Bonnie says again, setting off at quite a pace to crawl towards him. She meets him at the kitchen doorway and he swoops down to scoop her up into his arms. 'Hello, my little Bonbon.' He blows raspberries into the side of her neck, making her squeal with delight. 'Oh,' he says, suddenly noticing Anna at the table. 'Hello.' I can hear the slight question in his voice.

'This is Anna,' I say. 'The lady I told you about, who found Oscar for us.'

'Of course!'

'Anna, this is my husband, Simon.'

Simon smiles as he approaches her, arm extended. 'Thank you, Anna,' he says, his smile broadening as he clasps her hand and holds it for a second too long. 'We're extremely grateful.'

I watch Anna closely as she shakes Simon's hand. I always watch women when they meet Simon, but Anna only smiles politely, and it's her that breaks the handshake first.

'I'd better go and let you get on with your evening.' Anna gets to her feet and swings her bag over her shoulder. 'Cheers for the coffee,' she says. 'It was lovely to meet this little angel.' She smiles at Bonnie, who's still sitting in the crook of Simon's arm. 'You are such a good girl, aren't you?' She touches her finger to the tip of Bonnie's nose.

'Deh!' Bonnie says, looking serious as she nods. We all laugh.

'And where's Oscar? I should say goodbye to him.' As if on cue, he appears, weaving a figure of eight around my legs. She bends down and tickles him under his chin causing him to purr ecstatically. When she straightens up, she turns to me and holds her hand out. 'Lovely to meet you,' she says. 'I never even asked – what's your name?'

'Oh, my goodness, sorry – I'm Emily. Emily Mason.' I take her hand. Her skin is cool, cold, even.

'Who knows,' she says, her eyes smiling into mine, 'maybe we'll bump into each other again at some point.'

'Maybe we will,' I say, and find myself adding, 'I only work Tuesday to Thursday at the moment, so I'm out and about more.'

'Good to meet you, Anna,' Simon calls over his shoulder as he takes a beer from the fridge.

I follow her to the front door. 'Maybe we . . .' I start, then I hesitate. Do I really want to do this? Anna isn't the sort of person I'd normally be friends with. I know that makes me sound snobby, but she's not the sort of person I'd normally meet. I feel strangely drawn to her, though. Or maybe it's the wine, clouding my judgement. But when she turns to face me, her expression is open and expectant. 'Anna,' I smile, 'I still don't feel I've thanked you properly. Do you fancy meeting for a coffee one day?'

CHAPTER FIVE

It's Friday, and I'm in a good mood as I collect our takeaway from the Thai place while Simon bathes Bonnie and puts her to bed. As I walk out of the restaurant holding the carrier containing our supper, I glance around at the diners. We used to come here a lot before Bonnie was born, and I feel a slight pang of envy as I look at the couples drinking wine and chatting over dishes garnished with elaborately carved vegetables. It's ages since we've been out. We try to make Fridays a bit special – it's often the only day Simon doesn't have a meeting. Before Bonnie, we'd have gone out for a drink, then a meal, then maybe a film before coming home and having sex on the nearest horizontal surface. Or against the nearest vertical one. The memory makes me smile. These days it's a takeaway, a bottle of wine from Sainsbury's, and a film on Netflix before tiptoeing past Bonnie's room and trying not to make too much noise as we fall into bed – sex has to be quieter once you have kids.

I never realised how much having a baby would affect our sex life. We're lucky if we manage once a week these days, and it seems to always be on a Friday or Saturday night. Gone are the long, delicious Sundays when, after spending the morning reading the papers, we'd open a bottle of wine and linger over a lazy lunch. Then we'd look at each other across the table, and the next minute we'd be running up the stairs, laughing and stumbling our way to the bedroom. Sometimes, we'd stay there all afternoon. Desire ripples down through my belly at the memory. I wonder if there's any chance my mum would have Bonnie overnight tomorrow? I dismiss the idea as I let myself back into the house. She probably would, but with such bad grace that it'd spoil everything anyway.

I'm humming to myself as I unpack the plastic takeaway boxes and tip the free prawn crackers into a bowl. I always say I'm going to refuse them, just to cut down *slightly* on unnecessary calories, but I never do. I put plates in the oven to warm and pour myself some wine while I wait for Simon. I would have thought he'd be down by now. I don't want to shout up in case Bonnie's only just dropping off, so after a couple of minutes, I go to the bottom of the stairs and listen. At first I think he's still reading her a story, but then I realise that it isn't his story voice. He's on the phone, but speaking so softly I can't make out what he's saying. I go back into the kitchen and wait. But after another few minutes, I go up quietly so as not to wake Bonnie. He's standing in our bedroom with his back to me. 'No,' he's saying. 'I haven't told Emily yet.'

I freeze. What hasn't he told me? Instead of going in to make 'supper's ready' signals at him, I find myself standing still, one hand on the banister rail, eavesdropping. 'I know,' he says. 'Yeah. Yeah, okay. See you tomorrow.' He turns and starts as he sees me.

I force a smile. 'I was just coming to tell you the food's getting cold.'

'Sorry, I didn't know you were back or I'd have come down.'

He follows me down the stairs in silence. He knew I'd be back with the food any minute, so why not have the phone conversation downstairs where he'd see me come in?

'Ooh, that smells good.' He takes the plates out of the oven and puts them on the table, then starts taking the lids off the plastic containers.

'Who was that on the phone?' I try to sound casual.

'Oh, only Marcus.'

'Oh yes?'

He busies himself with the food, spooning sticky rice onto his plate, then the green curry. Why isn't he saying anything else? I help myself to the pad thai as he tops up my glass and pours some for himself. 'Cheers,' he says, and we clink glasses.

For a couple of minutes, we chat about the food, how nice it is, how we've probably ordered too much again. I take a mouthful of wine. 'So,' I'm still trying to sound casual, 'what were you and Marcus being so secretive about?'

He looks up sharply. 'What do you mean "secretive"?'

'Well,' I'm concentrating on my plate, 'you were tucked away in the bedroom, talking more quietly than usual, and when I came to tell you the food was here, I couldn't help overhearing you say you hadn't told me yet.' I can feel my face going red, my heart rate speeding up, my good mood rapidly disappearing. He looks irritated.

'I wasn't *hiding away* as you put it, I was—'

'I didn't say *hiding away*. I said *tucked away*.'

'Same difference.'

'Are you winding me up?' He knows how much this expression makes my English teacher hackles rise, and sometimes he says it just to make me reel off examples of *actual* 'same differences'. I wait for him to continue, but he carries on forking food into his mouth.

'So are you going to tell me, then?'

'Tell you what? Oh yes,' he grins, 'the thing I haven't told you yet.'

Although I'm irritated by the teasing, I can feel the tension easing, my shoulders relaxing. He wouldn't be grinning if it was something bad, would he? 'Yes, what haven't you told me yet?'

'Just that I'm going to be out tomorrow evening. And most of the afternoon as well.' He looks up at me, contrite now. 'Sorry, Em. I meant to tell you before but there's been so much going on at school, it went out of my head.'

I nod. 'Okay. Where are you off to?'

'Bike ride with Marcus, Andy and another mate of his – Dan, who I haven't met yet, but Marcus says he's a nice bloke. It's his birthday – Dan's – so we're going to ride out to Keston, maybe further if we're not too knackered. We'll find a nice country pub for a rest and refuel before heading back to Bromley, where Dan lives. Then we're going out for a curry and a few beers, so I'd better take a change of clothes.'

I feel a flash of discomfort, simply because I know Andy is newly single, and when Andy goes *out* out, it's with the prime objective of picking up women – or so Marcus says, anyway.

'So what time will you be going?'

'About half two, probably. I know it leaves you on your own with Bonnie all afternoon, but I can take her out for a couple of hours on Sunday morning if you like?'

'I've got lesson planning to do, so yes, that would be good.'

We carry on eating in silence. I wish the prospect of this night out didn't make me so uncomfortable. I've never minded Simon going out with his mates, not that he goes out very often, and I don't want to be that sort of wife.

'You're quiet,' he says after a while.

'You're not being exactly chatty yourself.' I can hear the edge in my voice, and feel the slight tension in the air.

'Are you pissed off because I'm going out?'

'Of course not.' Our lovely Friday evening is slipping away and I really want to bring it back. 'Sorry, I'm . . . I don't know, it's been a tough week. I know I'm only doing three days, but it feels like I'm running up the down escalator all the time, trying to keep on top of the planning and marking, not to mention the house. I'm just so tired.'

'So I suppose an early night really means an early night

tonight then, does it?' He looks at me over his wine glass and raises an eyebrow. 'Or does it?'

This is my chance to try and put the evening properly back on track. I'm smiling as I pick up my glass and raise my eyebrow in return. 'Not necessarily.'

We look at each other for a moment and it feels like it used to in the pre-Bonnie days. I don't want the mood to disappear, so I make a conscious effort to push all the unsettling thoughts to the back of my mind. I've really got to stop dwelling on these things. Every time I start thinking about something, I end up blowing it out of all proportion. That's why I couldn't sleep last night – I started thinking about Sarah again, about all those meetings they're in together, and how casually she mentioned Bonnie's name, as though she's used to hearing about my family ... Oh for God's sake, I'm doing it again. *Stop it, Emily.* I take a swig of wine. 'So,' I smile at Simon, 'I haven't even asked you how school was today.'

'Oh, the usual.' As we finish eating, we chat about his day and mine. I tell him how Bonnie got on at the toddler group, he relates a couple of anecdotes from school. He doesn't mention Sarah, and I'm not sure if that's good or bad, but I'm not going to think about her any more tonight.

'Coffee?' I say as I put the plates in the dishwasher.

He nods. 'Yeah, okay.'

I switch the machine on and reach up to the cupboard for the coffee cups, but then Simon is behind me, and he catches my hand in his. 'Tell you what,' he says, turning me round and bringing my fingers to his lips. 'How about we take the wine upstairs and finish it in bed? If Madam's going to wake up, it probably won't be until later.' He leans down, lifts my top and puts his lips against my skin, sending delicious ripples down through my stomach. 'Which means more chance of an uninterrupted shag.'

I smile as I run my hand through his hair, cupping the back of his head as he kisses my midriff. 'So,' I murmur, 'do I take it you've changed your mind about coffee?'

'Fuck the coffee.' He unbuttons my jeans and starts to pull down the zip, kissing below my belly button at the same time. And then before I know it, we're sinking down, so smoothly I barely notice the hardness of the kitchen floor as he pulls my top over my head and helps me wriggle out of my jeans.

The sex is fast, urgent and just a little bit rough, but we both cry out as we come, knowing the kitchen is far enough away from Bonnie's room for us to safely make a noise.

'Oh my God.' Simon flops onto his back, still panting. 'That was amazing.'

I'm still panting too as I lie next to him on the wooden floor, looking up at the kitchen cupboards. After a few moments, I slide my arm around his waist and lay my head on his chest. I can hear his heart still hammering away beneath my cheek, and as it gradually begins to slow, I can feel the sweat starting to cool on his skin. I run my fingers through the soft, curly hair on his chest. 'This reminds me of before we had Bon.' Then I start to giggle.

'What's funny?'

'I was just thinking – we were so quick, that coffee's probably still warm.'

Later, we're in the sitting room watching the movie we'd planned to watch earlier, although I'm struggling to concentrate because my mind keeps slipping back to what we did on the kitchen floor. It's so long since we've had a quickie like that – it felt extra sexy.

I'm just beginning to get into the film when my phone rings. I glance at my watch. It's after nine thirty. 'Who's calling at this time?' I mutter. I stare at the screen.

'Aren't you going to get that?' Simon points the remote at the TV and hits pause.

'Private number again.'

'Again?' He shakes his head. 'Got to be another scam call, hasn't it? Ignore it.'

He starts the film, but the phone rings again, so this time I answer it. 'Hello?'

Nothing.

'Hello?'

But I know someone's there. And I have that feeling again, like I used to when I first had Bonnie; the feeling that we're being watched.

The following morning, I'm cutting Bonnie's Marmite toast into soldiers when my phone goes. I answer before I properly register that it says *Unknown Number* on the screen. 'Hello?' Silence. 'Look, whoever you—'

'Hello, my name's Amy, calling from Motor Claims Ltd. I understand you was involved in an accident recently what wasn't your fault?'

I resist the temptation to correct her grammar. 'I'm sure you could get a better job than this,' I say, and end the call. But it's got me thinking again about that silent call last night. That must be the fifth or sixth time it's happened in three weeks. I definitely got the impression there was someone there, listening.

'Da!' Bonnie says, pointing at the kitchen door seconds before Simon comes in, hair still wet from the shower.

'Morning, Bonbon.' He kisses her on the head, pinches one of her Marmite soldiers and then goes over to the work-top and switches on the coffee machine. 'Want one?'

'Got one, thanks.'

He whistles as he pours Cheerios into a bowl and fills it with milk before bringing it to the table. He scrolls through his phone as he lifts the spoon to his mouth, then dips it into the cereal again for more. As I watch him with his spoon, lifting and dipping, lifting and dipping, I can see something of the little boy he must have been thirty years ago.

'Weather looks good for the bike ride,' he says. 'What will you do while I'm out?'

'I might take Madam to the park, maybe go for a walk along the river path.'

He's nodding, not really taking it in. I reach across and run my finger along the back of his hand, and he looks up, curious. I smile. 'Last night was nice.' He looks confused for a second too long, and for a moment I think he's going to ask what happened last night, but then he gets it and grins. 'It was, wasn't it?'

A movement to my left catches my eye. The bay window looks out onto a small paved area and a fence that isn't high enough to shield us completely from anyone walking along the alley. By the time I turn to look, I can see only the back of a head so I don't know who it was. It'll be one of the neighbours – the alley runs along the side of our house from the road to another alley at the back where we keep the bins, and sometimes neighbours use it when they don't want to traipse grass cuttings or mud back through the house. 'Simon, we didn't even bother to close the blinds last night. Oh God, what if someone went past and looked in?'

'Nah, unlikely. Hardly anyone uses that alley.'

'They do. I couldn't see who it was but someone walked past just now.'

'Really?' Then he laughs. 'Maybe they want to see if there's going to be a repeat performance. We could put a sign up, sell tickets.'

I'm laughing with him, but I didn't like that feeling I had last night after that dodgy phone call, that sense we were being watched. Then I remind myself, that was two hours later. And anyway, realistically, if one of the neighbours had looked in and seen us having sex, they'd have probably fled in embarrassment. Even if they'd hung around and watched, they're not likely to then phone me a couple of hours later, are they? No, it's coincidence, that's all.

But it doesn't stop me from scanning the ground on the other side of the back wall when I take the recycling out. Sure enough, there are two cigarette ends lying next to the bin, just like before. I take a tissue out of my dressing gown pocket and use it to pick them up. Simon is still at the table finishing his coffee when I go back in. 'Look,' I say, unfolding the tissue. 'I found these behind the wall by the bin. No-one round here smokes. This proves someone's been standing there—'

Simon rolls his eyes. 'Oh, come on, Em. We've been through all this. It doesn't prove anything of the sort.'

'But why else would—'

'Look, as I've said before, there are a hundred and one reasons. It might be people in the house the other side of the alley, chucking their cigarette ends over the fence. Which is annoying, but it's not sinister. It might be someone walking through who happens to finish their smoke as they get to our back gate.'

'But hardly anyone even knows about that alley. It would have to be one of the neighbours, and why would they—'

'Maybe it *is* one of the neighbours, sneaking out for a crafty smoke because they're supposed to have given up.'

I concede that this is possible. When his parents came to stay after the wedding, they both kept making excuses to pop to the shops – we later found out they were each still having the odd cigarette but didn't want the other to know they'd failed to quit.

'Maybe I could ask around, see who—'

'That's ridiculous.' He's shaking his head. 'You need to let it go, Em. Stop worrying about it.'

'But what if—'

'Emily!' He bangs his hand down on the table. Not hard, but enough to show he's getting annoyed. Bonnie has stopped eating and is watching us intently. I see Simon notice. 'Look,' he says more quietly, 'this is ridiculous. I think you need to see someone. Get some counselling or something.'

'I don't need counselling, Simon. I'm not depressed, I'm just naturally concerned that someone might be watching our house.' I consider bringing up the cigarette end being squished out on my car a couple of weeks ago, but I stop myself – he made it clear at the time he thought it was just kids. 'There was a break-in down the road a few weeks ago – I don't think I'm being unreasonable.'

He stands up. 'Well, I think you *are* being unreasonable.' He sighs. 'That break-in was months ago, and they said it was an opportunist thief who took advantage because they'd left the garage unlocked.' He looks at his watch. 'Anyway, I'd better get moving. I'm meeting Marcus in twenty minutes.' He puts his arm around me and pulls me close. 'Look, I'm not having a go at you, Em,' he murmurs. 'But I honestly think you're worrying over nothing.'

I nod. 'Maybe you're right.'

'Da!' Bonnie shouts, not wanting to be left out.

Simon bends down and kisses her Marmite-coated face. 'Don't worry, Bonnie-Bon. I haven't forgotten you.' Then he picks up his phone. 'Right, I'm off. See you later.'

Maybe he's right, I think, as I wipe Bonnie's face and hands. Maybe I *am* worrying over nothing. Literally as I'm thinking this, my phone goes again. *Unknown Number.* I only hesitate for a moment before answering – it's probably Miss Motor Claims again.

'Hello?'

Silence. This time, there's no chirpy voice asking me about a recent accident *what wasn't your fault.* 'Hello? Who is this?' No reply. I think I can hear a faint movement, or maybe a breath, but I can't be sure. I close my eyes so I can listen more closely.

'Just hang up,' Simon mouths at me.

I shake my head and continue listening, certain that I can hear the person on the other end, standing there and listening back.

CHAPTER SIX

Bonnie woke up early, so we've all been awake since six. I'm so glad I'm not doing Mondays at the moment. I'm still in my dressing gown drinking coffee when my phone pings a text. Who could be texting me this early? I don't recognise the number, but then I read the first line. *Hello, it's Anna here – we met a couple of weeks ago when I found your cat. Hope I'm not being cheeky, but you said about maybe having a coffee some time and I wondered if you fancied doing that soon? Like even later today if you're not too busy?*

Anna. I'd forgotten all about her. I *did* suggest coffee. At the time, I was quite keen to meet up with her again. There was something about her I liked. I hesitate. Do I really want to start a potential friendship? I don't know much about her, but she did seem like a nice woman.

I'm still dithering when Simon comes down ready to leave for school. 'See you later.' He leans down and kisses me briefly on the lips. He's wearing a fresh-looking white linen shirt and he tastes of coffee and toothpaste. The combined smell of his aftershave and shower-fresh skin can still make my stomach flip, but I consciously try to ignore the frisson of desire.

'It'll probably be a late one again.' As he speaks, he turns to say goodbye to Bonnie so I can't see his face.

'Is that a new shirt?' I know the answer, but I ask anyway to see what he'll say. When did he buy it, I wonder, and why is he wearing a brand-new shirt to school?

'What?' He beams, eyes twinkling. 'This old thing?' I'm supposed to laugh at the cliché.

'No, seriously,' I say. 'I haven't seen it before. Where did you get it?'

He picks Bonnie up and starts the raspberry-blowing routine. 'Can't remember.' His face is buried in her armpit, so I can't see his expression as he says, 'I bought it a while ago. It's been knocking around in the back of my wardrobe and I thought it was about time I gave it an outing.'

Liar. 'Oh,' I say flatly. 'I don't remember you showing me.' He carries on making Bonnie giggle, pretending he hasn't heard. 'Why so late again? Another meeting, is it?' I try to keep the edge out of my voice but it's difficult. I know assistant heads have a lot of meetings, but it seems to be almost every night now.

'Yep, 'fraid so. There's always a meeting on Monday, you know that.' He puts Bonnie back down and picks up his keys and phone. I wish I didn't feel like this, this horrible suspicion creeping in every time some tiny thing happens. I tell myself there's nothing wrong with him buying a new shirt, and it's not his fault he looks so hot in it. I thought I might get all funny about him going out on Saturday night, but I didn't. It's *this* that bothers me more: school. *Sarah*.

'What are you up to today, then, Lady of Leisure?' He grins. He's saying it with good humour, but it rankles.

'Actually, I've still got some of last week's marking to finish – and emails I haven't answered. Plus I need to do a load of laundry *and* go shopping. And Bonnie doesn't entertain herself, you know.'

'All right, all right, you've made your point.' He's still grinning. 'I just wondered if you were doing anything interesting.'

I only hesitate for a moment. 'Yes, actually I am. I'm having coffee with Anna.'

'Anna?'

'You know, the woman who brought Oscar back.'

He looks at me quizzically. 'Really? I didn't know you were in touch with her.'

'We said we'd have a coffee at some point. We only arranged it recently.'

'Okay.' He nods, obviously surprised. 'Well, have a nice time.'

As soon as I hear the front door close, I pick up my phone and text a reply to Anna. *That would be lovely, and yes, I can be free today. What time works for you?*

We arrange to meet at the Costa near the *Cutty Sark* at 2pm. That should give me time to do my other stuff. I take the remaining exercise books out of my school bag. I should have done this yesterday when Simon took Bonnie to the park, but I was so tired after being up with her in the night – she's teething again – that I couldn't resist crawling back into bed.

I only get half of the books done before Bonnie starts to whinge. She's losing interest in her building blocks now and is throwing them across the floor in frustration. 'Stop that, sweetie, there's a good— Oww!' One of the blocks catches me on the corner of my eye. 'Bonnie, that hurt. You mustn't throw, okay?'

She shakes her head, but I'm not sure if she's agreeing that she mustn't throw or whether she's telling me she has no intention of doing as she's told. I try sitting her on my lap with her favourite soft toy, Mr Fox. But she keeps trying to grab my pen, and then she throws Mr Fox, hitting my mug so the coffee slops onto the table, only just missing the book I'm trying to mark. 'Bonnie, that's enough!'

Her lower lip wobbles.

I sigh. I consider taking her upstairs with me while I get dressed, but then I give in, turn the TV on and settle her in her highchair in front of Peppa Pig.

As soon as I walk into the bedroom, I see an empty carrier bag on the floor where Simon has tossed it in the general direction of the wastepaper basket. The new shirt. As I pick the bag up to put it in the bin, a receipt falls out. *Hugo Boss shirt*, I read. *Fabric: linen. Colour: white. Sale price: £89.* I knew it. But then I see the date – 14 December. More than three months ago. I bite my lip as I shove it into the bin, guilt flooding through me for not believing him.

I find I'm looking forward to coffee with Anna. I miss the chats I used to have with my old flatmates, Zoe and Tash. Zoe and I used to be quite close, but it seems to have dropped off since I got together with Simon, and I've hardly seen Tash at all.

Before I put my jeans on, I pause to look at myself in the mirror. My eyes are puffy from lack of sleep, with dark shadows underneath; my skin looks dull and dry. Then my gaze is drawn to the silvery white lines across my stomach, breasts and thighs. All that almond oil I rubbed in every day was a complete waste of time. My breasts are smaller and softer since I stopped breastfeeding, and my stomach looks paunchy. I struggle to zip up my jeans. A memory jumps into my mind from a week or so ago: Sarah, looking slim and gorgeous, standing too close to Simon in the corridor, apparently discussing something on the noticeboard. I can't get over how different she looks now, compared to that pale, tired-looking and slightly overweight woman who seemed to live in black leggings and shapeless tops. The first few times I saw her, her hair, which looked lank and unwashed, was scraped back in a harsh ponytail. Now she has a neat, trendy plait, or wears her hair pinned up on top of her head to show off her dangly earrings and elegant neck. Simon likes necks. He's always said he likes my hair short because it shows off my sexy neck.

I wonder how much time he spends looking at Sarah's

neck when they're in these meetings together. I find myself thinking about the fact that she knew Bonnie's name. I knew they were on speaking terms again because he told me, and the conversation's obviously on a more personal level now if Simon's talking to her about Bonnie. I wonder what else they discuss? Do they only talk in meetings and in the school corridor, or do they have coffee or lunch together on the days I'm not in? Christ, why am I doing this to myself? I pull my yellow cashmere jumper over my head. Thank God I decided to meet Anna this afternoon. I need the distraction.

Downstairs, Bonnie has tired of Peppa Pig and is banging her little fists on the tray of her highchair in protest. 'All right, sweetheart, let's get you out.' I take her back into the kitchen and try to interest her in her toys, but she toddles over to me and tries to climb onto my lap. 'All right, Bonnie-bons,' I lift her up, 'but let Mummy get on with this, okay? Then I promise we'll do something more interesting.'

I try to carry on marking as Bonnie reaches across to the fruit bowl. I pretend I haven't noticed, but then she starts throwing clementines. 'No, Bonnie.' I raise my voice, but not too much. 'No throwing.'

She grabs an apple and lifts her arm ready to throw it, but I quickly take it out of her hand. 'I said *no*. Now listen, Mummy's going to put you down for a few minutes, okay?'

'No!' she says as I try to set her down on the floor. 'No-no-no-no!' She shakes her head vigorously and kicks her legs. I end up pulling her back onto my lap. I rummage in my bag for a spare pen, tear a couple of sheets from my notepad and encourage her to scribble, which keeps her quiet for all of ten seconds, then she throws the paper on the floor, and as I'm leaning down to retrieve it, she pulls the book I'm marking towards her and rips the page. 'Bonnie! You naughty girl.' This time it's so sharp, her face crumples and she starts to cry. Oh my God, she's thirteen months old and I'm shouting at her. 'I'm sorry, sweetie.' I'm almost crying myself as I cuddle her. 'Mummy didn't mean to shout.'

I'm clearly not going to get any more done this morning. We've got time for a walk before I meet Anna, so I make some Marmite and grated cheese sandwiches that Bonnie can eat in the pushchair in the hope that she'll doze off as we're walking. It's sunny today but chilly, so I put her in her red duffle coat and ladybird mittens and we set off towards the river. Greenwich is busy as usual – there are tourists here all year round. I push the buggy along the river path, pausing every now and again so that Bonnie can watch the boats going up and down the Thames and delight in the little waves they leave in their wake. We walk as far as The Trafalgar, the pub where Simon and I used to go before Bonnie was born. Once the summer comes, maybe we'll come here again and sit by the huge open windows, sipping chilled white wine as we watch the river, its waters lapping at the walls a few feet below us.

I pull my scarf tighter as we head back. It's only as we're passing the Royal Naval College that I start to feel nervous. What am I going to talk to Anna about? What if we've absolutely nothing in common? I don't know anything about her, whether she's married, whether she has kids. I don't even know what she does for a living. She seemed to take to Bonnie, though, so that'll make it easier.

'Look at the big boat, Bonnie!' I stop in front of the *Cutty Sark* and turn the pushchair towards it. It looks magnificent in the spring sunshine. There are dozens of tourists milling around, taking photographs of its towering masts, or snapping their friends standing in front of it. When I was full time, it was easy to forget that we live somewhere so special, somewhere with historical significance. It's important to know about the past, and I'm going to make sure I pass on as much as possible to Bonnie so she knows who she is, where she comes from. My thoughts turn fleetingly to my mum and her reluctance to tell me anything I don't already know. Maybe if I mention it in the context of building a history for Bonnie, she'll be less reticent.

As soon as the coffee shop comes into view, I spot Anna standing outside, looking up towards the high street. She looks at her phone quickly before putting it back in her bag.

'Anna!' I wave as she turns towards me. There's a split second when I see the expression on her face before she breaks into a smile. She looks nervous; maybe she's worrying that we'll have nothing in common, too.

'Hello,' she says, beaming. 'I thought you'd be coming that way.' She gestures in the other direction.

'I decided to take Madam here for a walk along the river.'

Bonnie is looking at Anna with a mixture of suspicion and

curiosity. But then Anna crouches down and smiles at her. 'Hello, Bonnie. Do you remember me? I came to your house with your pussycat. Remember? It's lovely to see you again. And I like your mittens! Aren't they clever? They make your hands look like ladybirds, don't they?'

'Deh,' Bonnie says, immediately pulling off her mittens and holding them out to Anna.

'Ooh, thank you,' Anna says, turning the mittens round in her hands. 'They're lovely! Let's pop them back on you, shall we? Keep your hands nice and warm.'

She straightens up, still smiling, and we go inside. It's busy, but we find a table by the window, and as she helps me move chairs to make room for the pushchair, I have the feeling again that I've seen her somewhere before.

CHAPTER SEVEN

As I walk home afterwards, I think how nice it was having coffee with Anna. Much easier than I thought it would be. And the time went really quickly, especially as she had to dash off to pick her kids up from school. I never even asked her about her children. We seem to have spent most of the time talking about me and my life. I'm not sure how that happened. It annoys me when people talk endlessly about themselves, but Anna steered the conversation. She wanted to know everything, what school I went to, what sort of house I grew up in, what my parents were like and how I got on with them. It was flattering to have the full attention of someone who seemed so interested in me, but she hardly said anything about her own life, which is why I thought it would be good if I were to take her out for a nice long lunch, get her to talk about herself a bit more. Not only that, but I still feel bad that she wouldn't take the reward for finding Oscar, because it's obvious she hasn't got much money – she does about four different jobs, apparently. Apart from that, though, I didn't find out much about her at all.

School hasn't been too bad this week, but I'm still glad when Thursday afternoon comes around again. I pack the marking into my bag – eighty-four exercise books. I've also got loads of lesson planning to do this weekend, so it's not going to be as relaxing as I'd like. Before I had Bonnie, I'd have stayed and got most of it out of the way before going home, but Gemma doesn't work after five. As I step out of the classroom, I see Sarah coming along the corridor, looking gorgeous as usual in smart black trousers and a fitted white shirt, open at the neck to reveal a bold black-and-white 'statement' necklace. I never think to wear jewellery except for earrings. It gives her a sort of polished look. I don't normally see her around school very much, but thanks to a burst pipe on the floor above, I've had to use a different classroom for my Year 11s this week. I don't mind moving rooms, but it means I'm teaching on the same floor as Sarah's office, so I'm bumping into her a couple of times a day. I meet her eye and nod in acknowledgement. She'll be here until at least six thirty tonight, as will Simon, so I feel a bit self-conscious about leaving so early, even though I've got tons to do over the weekend. She nods in return. She's polite but not friendly, cool but not rude. I reflect on how Simon described her reaction when he told her it was over between them; he said she was 'dignified'.

I can hear her heels tapping along the floor as I put my

bags down to lock the classroom door, and I turn to watch her. She walks straight past her own office and, without knocking, goes into Simon's.

I stand there for a moment, dithering, then I pick up my bags and walk purposefully along the corridor in the same direction. I would have stuck my head around his door before leaving anyway, so why should I change that just because she's in there with him? I'm wearing flats – I can't do heels since I had Bonnie – and they make virtually no sound as I near Simon's office. I pause at the door. I can hear gentle laughter. My stomach is tying itself in knots, even though I know there's nothing sinister about colleagues laughing together. I almost feel like I should knock, but that would be stupid. I take a breath, grab the handle and push the door. They're standing either side of Simon's desk and they turn towards me, traces of amusement still dancing around their eyes and lips. 'Hey,' he says. 'You off now?'

'Yes, I have to pick Bonnie up by five. What time do you think you'll be home?' He's already told me, but for some reason, I want to say the word 'home' in front of Sarah.

'Probably about seven to half past, earlier if we're lucky.'

The 'we' means him and Sarah, both Senior Leadership Team, both professionals, as opposed to me, part-time subject teacher and not very good mum. 'Right, okay then. Well, I'll see you later.' I open the door again.

'Hold on, we're walking down there now anyway.'

So the three of us walk together along the corridor and down the stairs, Sarah and I saying nothing, Simon chattering away about the new safeguarding guidelines. 'Right,' I say again as we approach the main entrance. 'Have a good meeting.'

'See you in a bit.' Simon leans towards me and for a second I think he's going to kiss me, but of course he doesn't, not in school when there could be kids milling around. They know we're married, but we must never, ever let them see any hint of intimacy between us.

He and Sarah carry on along the corridor to the deputy head's office, where I presume they're having the meeting. I linger for a moment, watching them walk together, how their heads turn towards each other. Then Sarah says something and Simon laughs, throwing his head back. He used to say I made him laugh. But I can't remember the last time I said anything he found funny.

As I drive home, I replay all this in my head, analysing every moment, every expression on their faces, every nuance in their body language. Is this just colleagues working together, or is this ex-lovers, rekindling an intimacy they had before? They seem so easy in each other's company again. I sigh as I pull up outside Gemma's. I'm not doing myself any favours by dwelling on this, and I hate being this suspicious, but I can't ignore the fact that he deceived both of us. He didn't tell Sarah about me, and he didn't tell me about Sarah. Not until she was about to come back from her mum's, anyway. It was flattering to hear that he was so in love with me that he'd gone into denial about his relationship with her. But now I can't help but wonder if I'm in denial, too. If he could forget about her so easily because of me, what's to say he can't forget about me equally easily, and fall back in love with her? Surely he must compare us, even if he doesn't do it consciously.

Maybe I'm just feeling vulnerable at the moment. The silent phone calls are unnerving me. There were two more over the weekend, and another last night. There's no logical reason that they should be anything to do with Sarah – what would be the point? Unless it's some weird way of letting me know that she's there, present in our lives. Or that she has some control? Oh, I don't know. I'm driving myself crazy here.

As soon as I collect Bonnie, I feel tons better. She babbles away happily as we walk from Gemma's to the car, and as I strap her into her car seat, she plants a wet and unsolicited kiss on my cheek, lifting my spirits instantly and making me smile. 'Thank you, sweetie.' I kiss her back, breathing in the fresh peach scent of her skin.

It's Saturday morning. Simon's gone out on his bike again, looking slightly ridiculous. I'm sure he thinks he looks sexy in all that Lycra, but it's the one time he really doesn't. Before I had Bonnie, we'd go out together on our bikes at weekends – just a leisurely, non-Lycra-enhanced cycle ride out into the country – but I don't think my bike's been out of the garage in eighteen months. I miss things like that, especially as we had so little time together before Bonnie came along. Sometimes I feel like I never really got to know Simon properly before our lives changed so much.

I sigh as I clean up the fallout around Bonnie's highchair. I'm gearing myself up to ask my mum if she'll babysit so I can have lunch with Anna next Friday. Originally, I'd suggested Saturday so Bonnie could have stayed with Simon, but Anna works in a pub at the weekends, and for the next four Saturdays, apparently, she's working lunchtimes as well as evenings. Once I've tidied the kitchen, hung up the first load of laundry and put the second lot on to wash, I can no longer put it off. I reach for my phone. She doesn't answer straight away, and with each ring my urge to hang up increases. I'm about to end the call, telling myself I'll try again later, when she picks up. I take a breath. 'Hi Mum, it's me.'

'Oh, hello darling. What can I do for you?' Which puts my back up immediately. She makes it sound like I'm calling a shop or a plumber or something. Why can't I just call for a chat? But of course that's not why I'm calling, and my mother's unerring instincts have clearly forewarned her that a babysitting request is coming.

'Actually, I do have a favour to ask.' She doesn't say anything, so I continue. 'I was wondering if you'd be able to have Bonnie for a couple of hours on Friday.'

'Friday next week? I'll have to have a look at my diary. When you say a couple of hours, can you be more specific?'

'Um, well, it'd probably be more like three hours, I guess. I'm meeting a friend for lunch and we'll have drinks, so I won't take the car. So by the time I've got her to yours on the bus . . .' I'm thinking aloud. I should have thought this through before.

My mother sighs a small, irritated sigh.

'Unless . . . I don't suppose you could pick her up?'

'Darling, give me times, please. It's all very well saying you're going to lunch, but that could be anything from noon until two thirty, and you could be gone anything from an hour to three hours, so . . .'

She *always* does this. Never says, *yes, fine.* I do a quick calculation in my head. If I get ready first, drive Bonnie to my mum's then drop the car back here and walk to the restaurant . . . 'If I dropped her off, it would probably be about twelve fifteen until, um, allowing for the bus back, three thirty to four-ish?'

She doesn't say anything.

'Or if you were able to pick her up, especially if you could drop me at the restaurant, it wouldn't need to be until about ten to one.'

'Hmm, it's a bit tricky, I'm afraid. I'm frantically busy as you know, but I suppose if you're really stuck, I'll see what I can do. I'd have to make a few phone calls, see if I can shuffle things around.'

Much as I want to ask what things, and whether those things are really so important they couldn't be put off until another day, I know I'll regret it if I do. Instead, I take a breath and say, 'No, I'm not stuck. Not at all. I'll ask the childminder to have her. I was going to do that anyway – I thought you might like to spend some time with her, that's all.'

This time I sense a slight discomfort. I have successfully ruffled my mother's perfectly preened feathers.

71

'Of course I like to see Bonnie whenever I can, darling, but you know what a busy life I have. I need a bit more notice.' There's a pause. 'I like to see you as well, but you hardly ever pop over. I mean, when's the last time *we* had lunch?'

Typical of my mother to turn the conversation round so that I'm the one who feels guilty. But then I remember. 'Actually, we had lunch the week before last.'

'I mean a *proper* lunch, at a restaurant, just the two of us. Shouldn't be too difficult now you're only working part time.'

'Mum, I've told you before, it's not that easy. Even though I'm not in school on Mondays and Fridays, I still have planning and marking to get through. Honestly, I'm sure you think I spend my days off lying on the sofa eating chocolates.'

She ignores me. 'Maybe it *would* be best if your childminder friend were to have her . . .'

'Gemma isn't a friend, Mum, she's a professional childminder and I pay her to look after my daughter so that I can go to work. But yes, I'm sure we can fit in lunch at some point.'

The next thing I know, she's reeling off dates from her diary. I'm not sure how we've got to this so I suggest we look at dates another time as I try to bring the conversation back to next Friday. She's obviously not going to have Bonnie, and I can't help my irritation seeping through into my voice. 'Maybe I should have asked you sooner. I thought a week's notice would be enough.'

'It's not—'

'Almost a week, then. But like I say, don't worry, it's fine.

Gemma adores Bonnie, so I'm sure it won't be a problem.'
I say it as though I'm completely confident about this, but
Gemma's never that keen to do extra sessions, and I often
feel I have to grovel as much with her as I do with my mum.

'I adore her too, you know I do.' There's a slight pause.
'So let me know if that doesn't work out, and of course I'll
have her.'

'Okay. I'll do that. Anyway, I won't keep you chatting if
you're busy.'

Busy means she doesn't want to miss any of her usual
activities with the various clubs, groups and classes that she's
started since she retired from her role as a magistrate – there's
the wine-tasting group, walking group, book club, bridge
club, art class, poetry appreciation, yoga. There are probably
a few more by now – I lose track. I'm glad she has so many
interests, I really am. But I wish one of them was me. It's not
that we never spend time together – she's happy to chat to me
on shopping trips or in restaurants. But it's always superficial,
and often in public, so if I bring up the Forbidden Subject,
she can brush aside awkward questions with a nervous laugh,
chiding me gently for 'getting all serious'. I can't remember
the last time we had a proper conversation about ourselves,
about our lives.

'Oh, don't rush off,' she says now. 'I've got an hour or
so, then I've promised to play a round of golf with one
of the ladies from my walking group. Now, tell me how
everything's going. How's Simon coping with being the
assistant head?'

'Fine,' I say. 'And as I said before, he's *one* of the assistant heads. You're confusing it with the deputy head.'

After I get off the phone, I am *so* tempted to call her back and say actually, Gemma can't have Bonnie after all, so I'll take you up on that offer. But I chicken out.

CHAPTER EIGHT

By the time I've dropped Bonnie at Gemma's, parked the car back at home and walked to the restaurant, I'm a couple of minutes late and Anna is standing outside. She's dressed up – heels, earrings, a fitted black jacket over a pale grey wool dress. I instantly wish I'd made more effort.

'Anna!' I give her a hug, but she stiffens slightly. 'Have you been waiting long?'

'No, only a couple of minutes,' she says. 'Ooh, what's that scent you're wearing? It's lovely.'

'Jasmine – it's an aromatherapy oil. I can't wear perfumes at all. They always smell lovely in the bottle, but when I put them on my skin, they turn into Eau de Cat Wee.'

She laughs.

'Come on,' I say. 'Let's go in. You look lovely, by the way.'

Anna beams. 'So do you.'

Which is rubbish, obviously, but it's sweet of her.

A smiling waitress shows us to our table and hands us

both a menu. 'This is absolutely my treat,' I say, 'and I'll be offended if you don't have three courses, plenty of wine and a boozy coffee.'

'I'll do my best, then.' She smiles. 'I don't want to offend you.'

We go for a sharing platter of olives, sun-blush tomatoes and artisan breads with herb butter, and for the main course, Anna says she'll have the same as me because she's never had scallops before. When we've ordered, she looks around, exclaiming at the beautiful artwork on the walls and admiring the pristine pink-and-white table linen, sparkling glassware and gleaming silver. 'It's lovely here, isn't it?' she says. '*Well* posh. Do you come to places like this all the time?'

'It is a bit posh, I suppose. I've been a few times.'

After the waitress has poured the wine and we've clinked glasses, Anna asks who's looking after Bonnie.

'She's with the childminder – same place she goes Tuesday to Thursday. I asked my mum to babysit, but she usually finds a reason not to be available. She loves Bonnie to bits,' I explain as we pick at our starter, 'but she doesn't particularly enjoy looking after her when I'm not around. Not for more than an hour or so, anyway – she's terrified she might have to change a nappy, or risk getting Marmite on her Hermès blouse.'

'So how—' Anna begins, but I interrupt. 'So what about you?' I top up her glass and refill my own. 'How do you manage with babysitting? Does your mum help out?'

'No,' Anna takes a sip of her wine, 'I don't have children.'

'You don't . . .' I stop, a breadstick halfway to my mouth. 'But that day we met for coffee – didn't you say you had to dash off to get to the school by three twenty?'

'I was picking up my neighbour's little boys. I sometimes look after them after school until their mum gets home.' She pops an olive into her mouth.

'Ah, I see. Sorry, I just assumed.'

'I'm cheaper than a childminder, so it suits her, and it suits me, too – I love the boys, it fits in with my other jobs and it's a few extra quid a week.'

When she told me about the other jobs, cooking in a pub kitchen, cleaning, delivering leaflets and buying up old crap – her words – and selling it on eBay at a profit, I assumed she was doing them to fit in with her kids being at school, so I ask why she isn't doing something more settled and better paid. She says she likes the variety, and she makes the eBay selling sound like fun. Her face comes alive as she tells me how she recently bought a '*well* nasty little china ornament' for a fiver and sold it for over sixty pounds. What she enjoys most, though, she says, is the babysitting, because she'd always wanted to work with kids.

'Why didn't you?'

'I never got any qualifications. I didn't like school. Well, school didn't like me. I bunked off a lot.'

'That's a shame. One of the reasons I became a teacher was to try and make sure at least some of them would have a positive experience.'

She shrugs. 'It might still happen one day. I grew up with little kids around so I've got loads of experience.'

I'm about to ask her more when the waitress appears with our mains, setting them down with a flourish and then expertly refilling our glasses, one hand tucked neatly behind her back. 'Enjoy, ladies.' She gives a half bow and disappears.

I raise my glass. 'Cheers.'

Anna smiles and clinks her glass against mine. I'm conscious that I'm drinking more quickly than she is. I should slow down.

'So, you were telling me about—' I'm about to ask about her family when she cuts in. 'This is gorgeous! I can't believe I've never tried scallops before. Are they easy to cook?'

'I don't know – I'm not much of a cook, to be honest.'

'Oh, I love cooking. Meals you make at home are so much nicer than the crap you buy in the shops, and cheaper. Best thing is when you can make dead nice dinners out of nothing. You know, when you open the fridge and there's, like, one potato, half a tin of beans and a dried-up bit of old cheese? I betcha I could make something out of it. Like that programme that used to be on telly, *Ready Steady Cook*.'

'I'm the opposite. I can have a fridge full of top-quality ingredients and I haven't got a clue what to do with them.' Shit. I almost clap my hand over my mouth. There's me swanking about high quality ingredients when Anna's just told me how hard-up she is. 'Sorry. That sounded like I was showing off. I didn't mean it like that.'

Anna smiles. 'No worries.' She pauses. 'You know, I could come round one day and have a look in your fridge, give you some ideas.' She stops. 'Look at me, inviting myself round to yours! Sorry!'

'Don't apologise – I would love that!'

She smiles again. 'Really? Let's do that, then.'

We eat in silence for a few moments, then I ask how many brothers and sisters she has.

'Pardon?' Anna looks completely thrown.

'Sorry, just going back to what we were talking about before. You said you grew up with lots of little kids. Do you have a really big family?'

She hesitates, and I wonder if it's a difficult subject for some reason. But then she says, 'Yes, quite big.' She forks more risotto into her mouth and spears another scallop.

I wait, but she doesn't volunteer anything else. 'So, brothers? Sisters? Both?'

She nods. 'Both. There's my big sister, Jess; Curtis, my little brother. Plus my little sister and loads of cousins. There was always a house full.'

'You're one of four? Wow!'

Anna continues. 'I was always looking after the little 'uns, taking them swimming, or up the park and that.' She takes a sip of wine, looking thoughtful, even sad. 'I know you said you were an only child, but did you have cousins around when you were growing up?'

'No. Both my parents are only children, too. Must be lovely to have a big family.'

Anna doesn't reply. She seems to be concentrating fiercely on her food. I top up her glass and empty the last of the Chablis into my own.

'I really need to slow down,' I say. 'I'm drinking way more than you.'

'You're entitled to,' Anna says. 'Don't take any notice of me – I'm a rubbish drinker.' She takes a tiny sip and then says, 'Tell me more about your mum and dad. I remember you saying you hardly see your dad these days, but what about your mum. Is she nice?'

'She's all right. She can be annoying, though. What about your parents? Are they still together?'

Anna sighs, takes the last mouthful of risotto and places her fork neatly on her plate. 'They died.'

'Oh, Anna, I'm so sorry.'

'It's okay. My dad died when I was little. It was a long time ago.' She touches the locket at her neck and slides it back and forth on its chain. 'I lost my mum when I was sixteen. That was hard, because she was a lovely mum. I miss her.' She takes a big swallow of wine, and it's the first time the level in her glass has gone down more than halfway. 'So do you know where your dad is now?'

'Spain, with his thirty-nine-year-old girlfriend – only five years older than me!'

'I'm thirty-nine, too,' Anna says.

She looks older, but I drop in a tiny white lie. 'I thought you were about the same age as me. So the big four-oh's looming, then?'

'Yes. It makes you think about things. You know, life and that.'

I want to know what Anna thinks about 'life and that' but before I can ask, the waitress returns to clear the plates. 'More wine, ladies?' She takes the empty bottle. 'Or maybe some Prosecco? We have a slightly sweet one that goes well with most desserts.'

'Ooh, I love Prosecco,' Anna says, then looks embarrassed. 'Sorry, I didn't mean . . .'

'Prosecco would be lovely,' I say to the waitress. 'It will go beautifully with the pudding.'

'Please,' Anna says, 'let me pay for the Prosecco. It was cheeky of me to—'

'Nonsense! I already said — three courses and plenty of booze, and it's my treat.'

She argues for a bit, but eventually gives in.

When the Prosecco arrives, along with two slices of chocolate tart garnished with physalis, crème fraiche and little swirls of orange sauce, Anna exclaims, 'They look like something off the telly!'

They really do look exquisite, and I can't resist taking a couple of photos on my phone. 'I have *got* to put this on Instagram.'

'I don't do all that social media stuff,' Anna says. 'Never seem to have time.'

I'm enjoying Anna's company. There's something about her that I feel drawn to; maybe it's the way she encourages me to talk. It feels . . . intimate. We've had a delicious meal, I've had enough wine to make me feel warm and smiley, and there's an almost full bottle of fizz in the ice bucket.

'Do you think you'll have any more kids?' Anna asks.

I'm slightly taken aback. 'Um, I'm not sure really. I adore Bonnie. She's part of me and I love her more than anyone or anything. But it's much harder than I expected, especially at first. She wasn't a good sleeper, and she cried a lot. I thought I'd deal with it easily. None of that *let your baby cry* rubbish. I honestly thought that if I picked her up as soon as she cried, she'd stop. Ha!'

'But she didn't?'

'No, she didn't.'

'I hate hearing babies cry. Whenever we had babies at the house,' her gaze flickers towards me and then away again, 'like, my cousins and that – I'd always pick them up if they cried, even when they were older, like Bonnie's age. What is she, about one?'

'Almost fourteen months.'

'Ahh, I love them at that age.' She takes a sip of wine.

'It's getting easier,' I say. 'When I first had her, I worried a lot. Frightened she'd die if she missed her feed or got too hot or too cold. Mad! She woke up a lot at night, so I was only getting a few hours' sleep. Honestly, I've never been so knackered in my life.'

'That must've been hard.'

'I was a bit rubbish then, to be honest. Bursting into tears all the time, scared to take my eyes off her in case something happened. Anyway, to answer your question, probably, but not for at least another year or two.'

My mind drifts back to the labour, the stitches, the sore nipples, the wondering if I'd ever *want* to have sex again, never mind be able to. Then the weeks of crippling tiredness, the crying, the paranoia. Could I really go through that again? I reach for the bottle in the ice bucket. 'Ready for a top-up?'

'Thanks.' Anna pushes her glass across the table. Despite saying how much she loves Prosecco, she's hardly touched hers. She leans back in her chair and takes a sip. She can't have had more than one glass out of the first bottle of wine, and I've barely topped up her Prosecco, which means I must have had more than a bottle already. The fizz isn't very strong, so maybe that's why I don't feel too drunk. And anyway, it's my day off, I'm having lunch with a girlfriend for the first time in for ever, so fuck it, why shouldn't I have a drink?

'So,' Anna says, 'how did you and Simon meet?'

'I'll tell you another time,' I say. I don't really want to think about Sarah right now, and anyway, she's doing it again, encouraging me to talk about myself. 'You're a good listener, aren't you?'

'I try to be.'

'My other friends ...' I notice how I automatically say 'other', suggesting I definitely regard Anna as a friend now. 'My so-called other friends,' I continue, 'seem to only want to talk about themselves. Don't get me wrong, I like hearing about what they're up to, but it would be nice if they'd ask how *I'm* doing once in a while.'

'They don't sound like very good mates to me,' Anna says. 'Why do you stay friends with them?'

'Well, you just do, don't you? I haven't fallen out with them as such, but I don't see as much of them since I had Bonnie. I guess they're not interested in babies because they don't have their own.'

'That's crap, though, isn't it? I don't have a baby, but I like hearing about them. I'm interested. One day I might see if I can do a course to learn how to be a nursery nurse.'

'That's a great idea, Anna! You should go for it. You'd be brilliant!' I'm starting to feel a bit tipsy now, and I wonder if the enthusiasm in my voice is a bit over-the-top. Anna doesn't appear to notice. She leans forward. 'Do you really think so? I'd love to do something like that.'

'Definitely,' I say. 'You're so good with Bonnie – you're obviously a natural with babies.'

Anna smiles that wide smile again.

'So, come on,' I say. 'Tell me about you. I know what you do for a living, but I don't really know anything else.'

Anna refills my glass and smiles. 'Yes, you do. You know I'm thirty-nine, that I spent a lot of time looking after little ones when I was young, that my parents are dead and that I bunked off school more times than I went in.'

'Okay,' I smile, 'fair enough. But I don't know the juicy stuff. Like, is there a Mr Anna, for example?' As I take a mouthful of fizz, I make a slurping sound. 'Oops!' I say, and we both laugh.

Anna shakes her head. 'No, and I prefer being on my

own. I lived with a bloke once, for almost a year. It didn't work out.'

'What went wrong, if you don't mind me asking?'

'Couldn't trust him. You can't really trust men, can you? Even the nice ones.' Then she looks up again. 'Oh, I didn't mean your Simon, obviously. I'm sure he's not like that.'

Is Simon 'like that'? Can he be trusted? I think again about him and Sarah standing so close together the other day, about the daily meetings they both have to attend. What if he's lying? What if there's no meeting tonight, and he and Sarah are having a cosy drink together, perhaps in that same wine bar he took me to when Sarah was away helping her mum to care for her dad? We'd been seeing each other for almost six weeks before he told me the truth.

I'm suddenly aware that Anna has said something.

'Sorry, I was miles away. What was that?'

'I said, are you okay?' She reaches for the almost empty bottle and shares the last few drops of fizz between us. 'You look worried.'

'No, I'm fine.' I drain my glass and put it back on the table where it makes contact too quickly, as though the table was nearer than I expected it to be.

'Tell you what,' Anna says. 'Shall we have one more glass? On me, this time.'

'Why not,' I say, 'but just put it on the bill.'

'No, really,' she insists. 'I'll be embarrassed if you don't let me pay for these, and then I'll feel like crap.'

I pause for a moment. I hadn't realised I might be

embarrassing her. I'm conscious of how expensive it is in here, but I don't want to make her feel bad, so I reluctantly agree.

'What would you like?' she says. 'More Prosecco, or another glass of wine?'

'Sauvignon Blanc, if that's okay. Just a small one, though.'

She ignores that and orders a large one, and a single glass of Prosecco for herself. I chide her half-heartedly. 'I'll be pissed as a fart at this rate,' I say.

She clinks her glass against mine. 'It's so kind of you to treat me to this gorgeous lunch. The least I can do is buy you a glass of wine.'

It's only when I'm about halfway through that glass that I notice the time. 'Oh fuck. Sorry, I need to message Gemma. I was supposed to pick Bonnie up twenty minutes ago.' As I try to key in the text, I realise that I've definitely had too much to drink. In the end, I give up on the text and call Gemma instead. 'Voicemail,' I say to Anna. 'Thank God!' I gush my apologies and say I'll be there in twenty minutes, half an hour, max, then I call across to the waitress for the bill. People are looking at me. Maybe that was a bit loud. Once I've booked an Uber, I put my phone in my bag and pick up my glass. 'I'd better neck this.' I take one mouthful, swirl the wine in the glass and finish it in two gulps.

'Shall I come with you?' Anna says. 'To pick Bonnie up, I mean. I could come back to the house with you, make sure you get home all right.'

'I'll be fine,' I say. 'I know I've had a couple of drinks,

but it'll wear off by the time I get home.' I'm slurring. I can hear it myself.

'What time does Simon get in?' Anna asks.

'God knows. Late again, I s'pose. Half seven, probably.'

Anna checks her phone. 'I could keep an eye on Bonnie for you while you just . . . rest.'

Guilt starts to creep in. I've allowed myself to drink way too much with barely a thought for my daughter. The waitress arrives with the bill and I pay with my credit card, knocking over my wine glass as I go to put the card back in my wallet. 'Oops, sorry! Good job it was empty.' I stand it up again. 'I've had a really, really nice time. How about meeting up again in a week or two? Another lunch. Or even just coffee?'

Anna beams. 'That would be great.'

'You stay and finish your drink. No need to rush.' I stand clumsily, jarring the table so Anna has to grab her glass to stop it from tipping over.

'Emily, there is no way I'm letting you go home on your own.' She stands, picks up her jacket and slings her bag over her shoulder. 'Come on, let's get out of here.'

This time I don't argue.

It's almost five when we arrive at Gemma's. Anna waits in the cab. The front door is open with a baby gate fixed across the hallway. Instead of unlatching it, I decide it would be quicker to climb over it, but as I do so my back foot catches the top of the gate and I fall onto my hands and knees on the hall carpet, just as Gemma's coming out of the playroom,

Bonnie toddling behind. I scramble to my feet. 'Tripped over the gate,' I say unnecessarily. I try a conciliatory smile. 'Sorry I'm so late, Gem.'

Why did I call her Gem? I never call her Gem. 'Obviously I'll pay you for the extra hour.'

Gemma is not impressed. 'It's not about the money, Emily. I know things can go wrong and anyone can be delayed, but let me know before collection time if it happens again, okay?'

'It won't happen again.' I scoop Bonnie up into my arms. 'Say bye-bye to Gemma, sweetheart.'

'Bye,' Bonnie says, waving.

I apologise again as I gather Bonnie's things, turning away as I speak so that Gemma won't smell the alcohol on my breath.

CHAPTER NINE

When I open my eyes, the first thing I'm aware of is the sweat pooling in the hollows of my collar bones. I'm lying on top of the duvet, fully clothed. The curtains are drawn, but it's not completely dark yet. I lean up on my elbow to peer at the clock, and that's when I remember. I had lunch with Anna, and a few glasses of wine. I stare at the clock and the numbers come into focus – 19:47. It can't be that late, surely? As I swing my legs over the side of the bed, I feel slightly nauseous. There are voices downstairs – Simon's home. Bonnie! My insides go cold as I try to remember where Bonnie is. Then I hear her babbling away happily to Simon. But no sooner has the relief washed over me than it ebbs away again as I strain to remember. Did I put her down for a nap? Maybe I put her in her cot and Simon got her up when he came in. She'd have been crying, for sure. I picture Simon, furious at finding her abandoned in her cot because her mother's too pissed to look after her.

I get to my feet but instantly feel dizzy and have to sit down again. Then I hear another voice downstairs – Anna! Of course! She was keeping an eye on Bonnie. But I don't remember much about arranging it. In fact, the last thing I remember is standing in Gemma's hallway after falling over the stair gate. I can't have drunk that much, surely? Shame is creeping up my body, up through my neck and into my head, tightening the top of my scalp.

They all look up when I walk into the kitchen. Bonnie is sitting on Anna's lap, *The Very Hungry Caterpillar* open in front of them. Gratifyingly, she slides off and toddles over to me. I pick her up slowly and carefully, although the movement still causes my head to swim and another wave of nausea to rise up. 'Hello, sweetheart.' I kiss her cheek and stroke her hair back from her forehead. 'Mummy's been to sleep. Have you been having a nice time?'

'How are you feeling?' Simon asks. I can't quite read his expression.

Anna smiles. 'You look better – you must have needed it.'

'I don't think I realised how tired I was. I've not been sleeping well lately. Anyway, thank you so much for looking after Bonnie.' I notice the saucepans on the back of the hob, a colander full of pasta sitting on top of one of them.

Anna follows my gaze. 'I hope you don't mind,' she says, 'but I thought while I was making some pasta for Bonnie, I might as well make enough you and Simon, too. I didn't think you'd feel like cooking.'

'Thank you. That's very kind of you. Did you manage to

find everything okay?' I don't remember asking Anna to feed Bonnie, but I suppose I must have done. Anyway, I'm glad she did – Bonnie would be starving by now.

'It's only a basic tomato sauce with a bit of garlic and chilli, but it's nice with some Parmesan cheese. The pasta's all cooked and everything, so it just needs warming up.'

'So Bonnie's had hers?'

Simon stands up now. 'Yes, ate every scrap, didn't you, Bon-bons?' He holds his arms out to Bonnie and turns to me. 'Why don't you get the table laid for supper, and I'll get her ready for bed.' He glances up at the clock. 'It's too late for a bath now.'

'It's okay,' I say. 'I can get her ready for bed.'

'No,' he says firmly. 'I'll do it.' As he carries her along the hallway and up the stairs, his voice lightens and I hear him ask her whether she'd like to wear the Peppa Pig jimjams or the teddy bear ones.

I pull out a chair and flop down onto it. 'What time did he get in?'

Anna looks up at the clock. 'About half an hour ago.'

'I don't know what to say, Anna. I can assure you I don't make a habit of getting drunk at lunchtime – I didn't realise I'd had that much. I'm so, so sorry.'

'Don't be silly. I'm glad I could help.'

'I can't thank you enough for looking after Bonnie. Honestly, I don't know what I'd have done without you. I can't believe I slept for so long. What did Simon say when he got in?'

'Nothing really. I told him I'd convinced you to have a lie-down because you'd had a headache all day, and that it was a good excuse for me to play with Bonnie. Which is true.' She grins. 'She's a pleasure to look after.'

I'm touched that she's tried to cover for me. 'You're an absolute legend.' I stand up and wander over to the hob. 'And thank you for doing this.' I take the lid off the saucepan and sniff the rich tomato-y smell. 'Smells lovely. You'll stay and have some, won't you?'

'Ahh, bless you,' Anna says. 'But you don't want me around while you're having your dinner. Anyway, I should get going – I phoned the pub to tell them I'd be late, but it's Friday night, so—'

'Oh God. I totally forgot you were working tonight! And now you're late because of me. I'm so sorry. Look, get an Uber and I'll pay. It's the least I can do.'

'No need, honestly. It's only a ten-minute walk from here.'

'Please, Anna, let me—'

'No, I'll enjoy the walk.' She picks up her bag and hangs it on her shoulder. 'Do you fancy meeting for coffee again soon?'

'Absolutely! I'll text you.'

Simon has already turned his lamp off.

'So,' he says as I climb into bed. 'How much did you actually have at lunchtime?'

'Sorry?'

'Come on, Emily. You went to bed in the middle of the

day, leaving our daughter in the care of someone we hardly know. You must have been quite pissed.'

'I was *tired*, that's why I slept for two hours.' Guilt is making me defensive. 'And yes, of course I had a couple of glasses of wine with lunch, but that doesn't mean I was pissed. Anyway, *you* hardly know Anna but I've spent a lot of time with her now, and I know how good she is with kids. She's brilliant with Bonnie, and Bonnie likes her.'

'She's nice enough, but she's not really your type, is she?'

'What *is* my type, Simon? Do you mean the NCT mums?' I think about Phoebe and Dorinda with their *haven't you got her down for baby shiatsu yet* and *surely you're not giving her processed cheese.* 'Or people like Zoe, who I've seen a grand total of, what, three times in the last year? Or Tash, who's barely spoken to me since I met you?'

He sighs, and puts his arm around me. 'They think I led you astray.'

Zoe, Tash and I were all on the PGCE more than ten years ago. We shared a flat. Zoe and I even taught at the same school for a while, but even when we all went our separate ways, we'd still get together every couple of weeks, and if we couldn't meet, we'd FaceTime or chat on the phone. But something changed after I met Simon. I slide my arm around him. 'No, it was me they were pissed off with. Because I didn't dump you the second I found out about Sarah.'

I feel his body tense at the mention of Sarah's name. I wish the conversation hadn't taken this turn because now Sarah's in my head again, along with those nasty suspicions that live at the back of my brain and keep creeping to the front.

'It is what it is,' he says after a bit. 'We can't keep beating ourselves up over it. We could have handled it better. But . . .' He sighs again. 'Let's not get into it now. It happened, we're here, we've got a beautiful baby daughter and a bloody nice life. You don't regret it, do you?'

'No, I don't.' I listen to the silence for a moment. *Leave it there*, I tell myself. But my brain seems intent on making things difficult. *It is what it is.* What does that even mean? He might as well have said *we're stuck with it.* 'Do you regret it, then?'

'Of course not.'

'Do you still think about her?'

'What?'

'Sarah.'

He pulls away from me. 'For fuck's sake, Em. What do you want me to say?' He sighs. 'This is stupid. Let's get some sleep.'

I sigh, too. I want to sleep, I want to stop thinking but my mind won't let me. 'If Sarah hadn't been away when I started at Woodview, would we still have got together? Or was I just a stopgap until she got back?'

'Oh come on, Em, we've been through this. Just leave it, will you? I hate it when you get like this.'

'What do you mean, *like this*?'

'Maybe it's because you had a drink at lunchtime, but sometimes I think you get a bit . . .'

'A bit what?'

He puts his hand behind his head as he turns onto his back. 'Oh, I don't know, a bit . . .'

'Go on, say it. Paranoid? That's what you were going to say, isn't it?'

After Bonnie was born, I *was* paranoid for a while. Terrified something awful was going to happen to her, convinced someone was watching the house, following me every time I went out and just waiting for an opportunity to pluck her from my arms and steal her away. I even freaked out when someone left a gift for her on the doorstep – a beautiful little Babygro. There was nothing to say who it was from, and I thought it was creepy. But everyone said I was overreacting. I used to get tearful, too. The health visitor said it was postnatal depression, so I saw a doctor, got some help, and I'm fine now.

'I didn't say you were paranoid. I was going to say you can overreact sometimes, especially when you've been drinking.'

'So I'm supposed to have lunch with a friend without having a glass of wine, am I?' I hear myself, poking at him with a verbal stick, but I can't stop.

'That's not what I said!' He shakes his head and sighs. 'There's no point talking about it while you're like this.' He sounds weary, and turns over without kissing me.

I take a breath, ready to reply, then bite my lip. There's a tiny voice in the back of my head telling me he's right. After a couple of minutes staring at his naked back, I pull back the covers. 'I can't sleep,' I say. 'I'm going downstairs to read for a bit.'

In the kitchen, I go to the fridge. There's an open bottle of wine in the door, and I'm half tempted to have a glass now. I may have had quite a lot at lunchtime, but all I had at supper was water. No, I tell myself, don't be ridiculous. Instead, I cut a slice of cheesecake and pour a glass of milk. After what I ate and drank at lunchtime, the extra calories aren't going to make much difference.

It's gone three when I climb back into bed, pleased with myself for resisting the temptation to eat more cheesecake. I close my eyes and try to focus on my breathing, but my mind soon drifts and I'm thinking about Sarah, and the phone calls where nobody speaks. I force myself to think about something else, and my thoughts settle on Anna. It's odd how close I feel to her already. I wonder what it would be like to have brothers and sisters and cousins? I picture the family she described, a big, noisy, happy group, getting together for barbecues in summer, or round the dining table at Christmas. Although my childhood Christmases were filled with presents, an enormous tree and fine foods, my overriding memory is of loneliness. It was usually just the three of us around the table. When I asked why I couldn't have a brother or sister, my mother would say, *All we ever wanted was you.* But I always got the feeling that I hadn't turned out to be quite what she'd wanted.

Although I'm still awake, my brain is starting to stream words and images and it isn't long before I drift into sleep and my thoughts mangle into a dream. I'm a child again, and I've discovered my real family is a big happy family like Anna's.

There are countless siblings and cousins, and we even have a dog, a golden retriever, asleep in its basket and starting to snore. I wake with a start. Simon's breathing noisily – maybe he was snoring. He turns over in his sleep and throws an arm around me, which makes me happy and sad at the same time – happy because I feel close to him again after the horrible distance between us earlier, and sad because I suspect that if he woke up now, he'd remove his arm and turn away from me. I move towards him carefully, so as not to wake him, and I nuzzle up against him, breathing in the warm, biscuity smell of his skin.

CHAPTER TEN

We're having coffee as usual – we meet regularly on Mondays now, often on Fridays as well – and Anna is stirring her cappuccino thoughtfully. 'I've been thinking,' she says. 'You know what you were saying last week about having to do your marking and stuff on your days off because there isn't time on your work days?'

I roll my eyes. 'Yes, it's a nightmare. I was up at six this morning to try and finish it before coming to meet you, but I've still got more to do when I get back.'

'I might be able to help you out.'

'Really? How do you mean?'

'Tell me if I'm sticking my nose in where it's not wanted, but you know I look after my neighbour's little boys once or twice a week? Well, turns out they're moving soon, so that'll be the end of that.'

I sip my coffee. 'Really? I bet you'll miss them.'

'I will. But after what you were saying about having to

pick Bonnie up from Gemma's and that, well I was thinking, maybe I could pick her up at about three or four on the days you work and look after her till you get home. You could pay me less than you pay Gemma – it would help us both out.'

'Gosh, that's a very kind offer. But it would be a big commitment.'

'Oh, I'd love it. You'd have to think about it, obviously, talk to Simon and whatnot. I could stay until half six or seven – later if you want. Then you could get your work done at school like you were saying.'

I think about this. Driving straight home instead of having to face Gemma at the end of a long day – it's an attractive proposition. And it would save time.

'Obviously, I'm not a registered childminder or anything, but like I said, I've had loads of experience, and I love Bonnie to bits.'

'It does sound like a good idea. Thing is, though, are you sure you'd want to do it on a regular basis? I know she's lovely and cute and all that, but sometimes she can be a challenge, especially when she's tired.'

Anna smiles that beatific smile again. 'I'm used to kids. It won't bother me, honest – some of the little 'uns I've looked after have been right little wotsits, but they're just kids, aren't they? And you never know what . . .' The smile falters and she looks away. 'Anyway, look, see what Simon thinks. Like I said, I wouldn't expect you to pay me the same as you pay Gemma, what with her being a proper childminder and that.'

'Oh, we'd pay you the proper rate,' I say, perhaps a bit too quickly. I ought to discuss this with Simon before making any decisions, but I already know we're going to do this.

Simon and I are having supper when I mention the idea, but he doesn't agree as readily as I'd expected. He still thinks we don't know Anna well enough, but I point out that it's only for a few hours three times a week and anyway, I've known Anna for six weeks now, which is as long as he and I knew each other before we decided to get married and have babies. He opens his mouth to say something but I see the power of this argument register, and he nods as he tears off a chunk of naan bread to mop up the last of the lamb dhansak. I made it from one of those cooking from scratch kits, so it *almost* counts as home-made. 'Okay, fair point.' He takes a swig of his lager. I pour more wine.

Simon finishes eating and pushes his plate away. 'Tell you what,' he says. 'Why don't you get her over for supper one night so we can both get to know her better? Friday or Saturday perhaps, when we haven't got school the next day?'

'She works Friday and Saturday evenings in a pub – I told you. Although I suppose we could invite her for lunch.'

'Good idea. Not next Saturday, though, because I'm going out on the bike.'

'Oh, again? You didn't mention that.'

'Yes, I did, I told you the other night. I'm going with Marcus. Only for a couple of hours, but we'll probably round it off with a ploughman's in the pub.'

'I'm sure you didn't.'

'I definitely did. You've just forgotten.'

He sounds so certain that it makes me doubt my own memory. There's no point in arguing, anyway. 'I'll make it the Sunday, then.'

'Good.' He stands up and kisses me on the head. 'Sounds like a plan.'

One of the things I miss about working full time is having my own form. You get to know the kids quite well and it becomes like a sort of family. As a part-timer, I'm always being asked to register other people's forms. I recognise a few of the names in this Year 9 group. 'Okay, 9C,' I say after calling the last name, 'off you go – *quietly*. Have a good day.'

'Miss?' There's a giggly little huddle of four girls around my desk, fronted by Jade Parker. Bright girl, likes to be the centre of attention. 'Is it true that Mr Anderson is your husband?'

'I suspect you already know the answer to that, Jade.'

'When did you get married, Miss?'

I ignore the question as I gather my things. It's best not to reveal anything personal. 'Come on, girls, you'll be late for first period, and so will I.' I usher them along with me as I walk towards the door.

Jade hitches her bag over her shoulder and falls into step beside me. 'If you'd of told me, Miss, I could of been your bridesmaid.' They all laugh.

'I'm sure you'll get your chance one day, Jade.' I smile as we reach the end of the corridor. 'Have a good day, girls.' But as I start down the stairs, Jade calls after me, 'And is it true that Mr Anderson used to go out with Miss Miles?'

For a second, the question stops me in my tracks, but I recover quickly and without turning to look at them, I call back up the stairs, 'Hurry up and get to your lessons, or you'll end up with a late mark.' I hurry down to the next floor without looking back.

For the next couple of hours, I'm distracted by work. The quiz I devised for the Year 10 group goes down a storm, and I'm surprised by a really good discussion about Romeo and Juliet's whirlwind romance in a revision session with my Year 11s. They're responding well to the text and asking interesting, insightful questions. Sessions like this make it all worthwhile.

But almost as soon as the pips go at the end of the morning, I think back to Jade Parker and her questions. Jade and her friends wouldn't have even been at the school then, so it's obviously still being talked about among the older kids, and Jade has clearly decided it's the sort of information that might be useful, possibly as a weapon. I used to get upset when kids deliberately said things that were hurtful or embarrassing, but then I read an article about the development of the teenage brain. Apparently, the parts of the brain that control empathy aren't properly developed at this stage, which would have been good to know when I was doing the PGCE. It doesn't make it much easier to deal with, but at least I don't take it personally anymore.

At lunchtime, I mention Jade's comments to Pauline when

I find myself sitting next to her in the staff room. Pauline is one of the older teachers here, and one the few who didn't start blanking me when they found out what had happened. 'I managed not to respond,' I say quite loudly – it's packed in here today, so it's not easy to make yourself heard over the hubbub of conversation and the hiss of the coffee machine. 'But I'm a bit concerned that won't be the end of it.'

'Year Nines? How the devil did they know? That lot would've still been at primary school.'

'I know, that's what I thought. Which means some of the older kids must still be talking about it. But why would they? It's almost three years ago now. Unless . . .' I take a mouthful of coffee, grimacing as I swallow. 'That milk's off.'

'Oh dear, it is, isn't it.' Pauline puts her cup on the low table in front of us. 'Wait until there's a lull at the machine and I'll get us another. What were you going to say?'

I hesitate. 'Well, I was just thinking. They do spend a lot of time together – Simon and Sarah. I know it can't be avoided, given that they're both assistant heads. But what if the older kids have noticed, seen them around together and made assumptions?'

Pauline doesn't say anything, but she looks thoughtful. 'Could be,' she says. 'But it's more likely one of the older girls has mentioned it for some reason and it's been picked up by Year Nines. You know what they're like with any scraps of gossip.'

'True.' Pauline has been teaching for over twenty years – eighteen of them at this very school – so I trust her judgement. She takes another sandwich from her lunchbox as I take a bite of my chicken and avocado wrap. Maybe she's right, though I'm still wondering why anyone would be talking about it three years on. Pauline finishes eating and brushes the crumbs from her lap. I don't catch what she says next because it's so bloody noisy in here, so I ask her to repeat it.

'I said, you're not worried, are you? About Simon going back to Sarah?'

I hesitate for a moment before replying. 'No, no, of course not.' She looks at me for a second or two before nodding. Then she smiles. 'Ooh look, there's a gap.' She picks up our coffee cups and heads over to the machine while I finish my lunch. I'm not entirely sure whether she was trying to reassure me or inviting me to confide my worries. I'm suddenly aware that Lisa, a maths teacher who was sitting next to Pauline on the other side, is on her feet, stuffing a pile of exercise books back into her bag. She catches my eye and we both nod in greeting. Then she picks up her phone and bag, and as she passes, she leans towards me. 'All I'm going to say is, in my experience, once a cheater, always a cheater.'

CHAPTER ELEVEN

I manage to put Bonnie down for a nap on Saturday afternoon, which gives me time to finish the worksheets for next week. I wonder why I feel so grouchy. Maybe it's simply envy. The fact that Simon can go off a bike ride with his mates whenever he feels like it. I don't begrudge him, I really don't, but I miss doing social things. Before I met Simon, Zoe, Tash and I would often meet up for coffee on Sunday mornings then spend a couple of hours poking around Greenwich Market. After that, we'd buy the Sunday papers to read in the pub while eating thick-cut, skin-on chips and drinking big glasses of chilled white wine. Bonnie's still asleep when I shut down my laptop, so I make myself some tea, pick up my book and take it through into the sitting room. It's a lovely, sunny afternoon, warm enough to sit outside, but if I do, I won't hear her when she wakes.

I read three pages but I'm not taking it in. I'm still thinking about lunchtimes in pub gardens with my friends before

I met Simon. I miss Zoe and Tash, especially Zoe. We've not talked much about what happened with me and Simon, but it's clear my friends disapproved as much as my colleagues. If I'm honest, my reaction would probably have been the same if it'd been them. *Not very sisterly, is it?* Zoe had muttered when I told her.

I pick up my phone, open up Facebook and check my notifications. When was I last on here? It's weeks since I posted anything. I don't seem to have time since I've been back at school. I hadn't realised how Bonnie would fill those two extra days off, especially now her daytime naps are getting shorter. Some of the mums at Soft Play were saying their little ones have already given up their morning naps. God, I hope Bonnie doesn't follow suit.

Scrolling down my timeline, I chuckle at a few memes and click 'like' almost automatically as I look at posts from people I haven't seen in the flesh for years. It's the usual collection – people I was at uni with, past colleagues, acquaintances, friends of friends and a few people I can't even remember meeting. I spend a while catching up with holiday snaps and the photos of kids and pets. My own timeline is similar – mostly photos of Bonnie or Oscar, or Bonnie *and* Oscar. My most recent post – weeks ago now – is a photo of Bonnie asleep in her cot, wearing the silver wellies she loves so much that she wouldn't take them off. The post has thirty-six 'likes' and nineteen 'loves'. I run through the names and find that Zoe has clicked the heart, and Tash has clicked 'like'. I feel an odd mix of relief that they're still responding to my posts, and sadness that this is the only contact we have these days. I click on both their timelines. Neither of them post much, but there are a few photos of them together, sometimes just the two of them, sometimes in a crowd, but not with people I know. Work colleagues, probably. Neither of them is still teaching. There's one of Zoe drinking cocktails with a man. I wonder if it's a new boyfriend? She'd just broken up with Adam last time we saw each other – more than six months ago.

I close Facebook and sit there for a minute, thinking about Zoe. Then I open up my email. There's a new one from my hairdresser's, a reminder about my appointment next week, and one from someone claiming to be minor royalty who wants to love me and make me happy and share his vast wealth with me. I open a new message. *Hey Zoe*, I type. *How are you doing? Writing this because I'm feeling a bit sorry for myself at the moment – so probably won't even send it, but I've got to get this off my chest. What happened, Zo? We used to be such good mates but now it feels like you don't want to even speak to me. I know you disapprove of me getting together with Simon while he was still engaged, and I totally get that, but does it have to mean the end of our friendship? We've never talked about it properly, but maybe we should, although if you really don't want to speak to me, I won't bother you again.*

As you know, when I met Simon, I had no idea he was with someone else. Some of the other teachers were a bit off with me, but I thought it was because I was new at the school. It was a total shock when he told me the truth. But by that time, I knew I wanted to be with him. We'd already talked about getting married, even about having children — Sarah didn't want kids, and that was a big problem for Simon, so they'd have split up anyway at some point. I know that doesn't make it any less of a betrayal, but I think it's relevant.

I pause. Do I even need to explain myself to Zoe?

I guess I should have ended it as soon as I found out and then waited for him to finish with her, but if I'm being totally honest, maybe I was scared he'd decide to stay with her after all. He swore to me that he'd been thinking about things while she was away and had been going to end it with her. I think I believe him, but sometimes, when I see them together at school, I wonder if he's regretting it. And then I wonder if I'm just being paranoid. Oh, ffs!!!!

For some reason, those exclamation marks make me feel slightly better.

I don't even know why I'm writing this. Maybe I'll send it, maybe I won't. Maybe, maybe, maybe.

I look again at the email. Oh, what the hell. Either she'll answer or she won't. I press send.

CHAPTER TWELVE

Usually when Anna and I have coffee, we meet in the afternoon so I can get stuff done in the morning, but when it's clear by eleven that Bonnie isn't going to go down for a nap, I message Anna to see if she's free to meet earlier. *Sure,* she replies. *Costa at 12?*

So instead of coffee, we end up having lunch. I insist on paying, because I know she doesn't have much money, and after all, it was my suggestion to meet earlier. Bonnie's still wide awake, and happily eats half my tuna and cheese toastie, a whole banana and a raspberry yoghurt. Anna plays peek-a-boo with her, making her laugh as though it's the funniest thing she's ever seen. Just as I'm thinking of gathering my stuff and making a move, Anna says, 'Let's have another coffee. And cake.'

'No,' I say. 'I'd better not. I've got shitloads to do when I get home. The house is a tip, I haven't done any ironing for days and the place is covered in cat hair. Not only that, but I *really* need to lose a few pounds.'

Her face falls. 'Oh, go on,' she says. 'Stay a bit longer. There's no point in me going home now because I've got to pick the boys up at three twenty. Let's share a cake – then it'll only be half the calories.'

I smile. 'It's tempting, but I really—'

'Please, Emily. You paid for lunch – you're always paying for stuff. Let me at least pay for coffee and cake.'

'You know I'm happy to—'

'I know, but I feel like crap if I don't ever pay. And if you stay a bit longer, Bonnie'll be tired and she'll probably drop off on the way home, then you can get your stuff done.'

Bonnie isn't showing any signs of sleepiness yet, but I suppose now she's eaten, she might be ready for a doze soon. 'All right, you've convinced me.'

So we share a salted caramel brownie with our coffee, and Bonnie has a shortbread biscuit. Anna checks with me first, but I almost look over my shoulder to make sure none of the NCT mums are in because I'm sure that even one biscuit would be frowned upon by the hummus and carrot-stick brigade.

We chat some more, and Anna tells me how much she's going to miss looking after her neighbour's little boys. 'I've had them at least once a week for over a year, but they're moving on Saturday, so today's the last day.'

'Ah, what a shame.'

'It'll be sad. But hopefully,' she leans over to grin at Bonnie, 'hopefully, your mummy and daddy will let me look after you soon, and that'll make it all better. Won't it, eh?'

Bonnie grins back and nods. 'Deh.'

'That reminds me,' I say. 'Still okay for lunch on Sunday?'

'Definitely.'

'Great.' I grab a baby wipe to clean Bonnie's face, then I start to pack away her things. 'I really must get going, or the day's going to disappear.'

'Hadn't you better change her before you go?' Anna says. 'Then you won't have to worry if she falls asleep on the way back.'

I feel a flash of irritation as, for a second, she reminds me of Phoebe, the NCT mum who seemed to be under the impression that I welcomed her advice on how to look after my own child. Annoyingly, Anna's probably right, and I acknowledge this with a nod. As I lift Bonnie out of her highchair, Anna hands me the changing bag. 'I'll keep an eye on your stuff,' she says.

As I get Bonnie changed in the loos, I run through a mental list of the things I still have to do today. I don't know how I let Anna talk me into staying this long. I look at my watch – it'll be almost three by the time I get home.

Back in the coffee shop, I strap Bonnie into the pushchair and retrieve my bag from under the table. 'Are you walking up to the school, then?'

'I don't need to leave for another ten minutes,' Anna says, 'so I'll hang about here for a bit. Have a look at the paper and whatnot.' She reaches across and picks up a copy of *Metro* from an empty table.

'Okay then. See you Sunday! Say bye-bye to Anna, Bonnie.'

'Bye.' Bonnie grins and waves.

Anna blows her a kiss. 'Bye-bye, my darling. See you soon.'

As I hurry home, I remember it's 2 May, my mum's birthday. I posted a card a few days ago but I'd better give her a call later. She'll be out with her golf friends now, and anyway, I really need to get on with stuff. When I was full time, I'd be at school until about six, and there was always planning at weekends, but I still seemed to have more time than I do now. Having Jenny in once a week to clean and iron helped a lot, but with my salary being virtually cut in half, it was an obvious economy. I totally underestimated how much time would be swallowed up looking after Bonnie. I glance down at my daughter, who has that fixed, glassy stare that suggests she's finally getting sleepy. I still get a kick out of that – *my daughter,* my flesh and blood, my own child. I slow my pace, crossing my fingers that she'll drop off before we get home.

Sure enough, by the time we arrive at the house, Bonnie's sound asleep. Carefully, I lift her out of the pushchair and carry her upstairs. For a moment, I stand there holding her, feeling the warmth of her perfect little body in my arms before I lay her in her cot.

As I plough through the ironing, it occurs to me that I haven't had a reply from Zoe. It's almost a week now, so maybe it isn't going to happen; maybe our friendship really is over.

I've just finished when Bonnie wakes up. She babbles to herself in her cot for a few minutes, but then she starts to grizzle. 'All right, sweetheart,' I call up the stairs as I put the ironing board away. 'Mummy's coming.' She grins when she sees me, her damp hair plastered to her head. As I lift her from the cot, I breathe in her warm, salty smell. By the time I've changed her and given her a drink, it's gone five and I still haven't vacuumed or done anything about supper.

I heat up some macaroni cheese for Bonnie and take a pizza out of the freezer for Simon and me. It's the second time we've had pizza this week – I really must do an online shop. The bag of salad leaves that was in the fridge has gone limp, but maybe Simon can pick some up on his way home. I rummage in my bag for my phone, but it isn't there. After checking my pockets, then the changing bag, then going through the pushchair, checking in the folds of the hood as well as in the shopping space beneath the seat, I'm convinced I've lost it. I check my handbag again, my stomach tightening as I do so. Calm down, I tell myself. I always do this, feel certain I've lost my phone if I can't put my hands on it immediately. Did I use it while I was in Costa? I remember throwing it into my bag after I messaged Anna this morning. I try calling it from the landline, but it goes straight to voicemail, which is weird, because I hardly ever turn it off. I check the whole house, even rooms I'm sure I haven't even been in today. The more I think about it, the more certain I am that I put it in my bag before I went out. I must have left it somewhere. I think about calling Anna to see if she remembers whether I had it out in Costa's, but of course without my phone, I don't know her number. I open up my laptop and google the number for Costa. They're sympathetic, and they even go and check the baby changing area in the loos for me, but no luck.

Bonnie's getting fed up with sitting in her highchair now, so I lift her down and try to interest her in her shape sorter, but she pushes it away in favour of her Fisher-Price phone. The irony. 'Deh,' she says, nodding importantly as she puts it to her ear, then hands it to me, gesturing to me to talk. 'Dada,' she says. 'Hello,' I say. 'Is that Daddy?' Bonnie grins her approval. I chatter away for a bit, then guiltily hand it back to her. 'Sorry, Bon-bon, Mummy's really, really busy. I'll play with you again in a minute, okay?' But Bonnie doesn't think it's okay at all, and we're soon into a proper tantrum. I thought tantrums weren't supposed to happen until the 'terrible twos', but Bonnie clearly hasn't read the book, and she throws herself down, screaming, her legs going like pistons and her feet in their little pink unicorn trainers pummelling the floor with such force that I worry she'll hurt herself. 'Come on, sweet-heart, stop that now.' I try to lift her but she throws her arms up and slides out of my grasp. Her face is red and there are huge tears on her cheeks. 'Bonnie, please darling, stop that.' But she just screams louder and carries on beating the floor with her feet. She's screaming so much she seems to be struggling to catch a breath. Tears of frustration and helplessness catch in my throat as I realise I have absolutely no idea what to do. What if she stops breathing? I've read that toddlers sometimes hold their breath and pass out during a tantrum. What if— And then I hear the front door. Simon! Oh thank God.

The kitchen door swings open. 'What on earth's the matter?' he says, dropping his laptop case onto the table.

'She's all right,' I say quickly, and as I start to explain the tantrum, Bonnie stops crying, picks herself up and toddles towards Simon, who sweeps her up into his arms. I have to turn away to hide the feelings I'm sure must be etched on my face. Then I feel guilty for feeling jealous. The important thing is that she's stopped, I tell myself, not that it's Simon who's managed to stop her. I can hear his voice, soothing, placatory, and I can hear Bonnie's shuddering sighs as she allows him to comfort her. 'I tried to pick her up,' I tell him, 'but she wouldn't let me.'

'Never mind,' he says, and I think he's talking to me until he says, 'Daddy's here now.' And I want to scream. But instead, when he takes her up to get her ready for bed, I burst into tears. Not only can I not keep on top of the bloody house stuff, but I can't even deal with a toddler's tantrum. *And* I've lost my fucking phone.

'Where did you have it last?' Simon says when I tell him.

I almost laugh. Why do people always say that when you've lost something? I can see by his exasperated expression that he's about to tell me I should be more careful – he's one of those annoying people who never loses anything. But before I can reply, the doorbell goes. 'I'll get it,' I say. I recognise her silhouette through the glass. 'Anna!'

'Hello.' She delves into her bag. 'Your phone.' She holds it up triumphantly and then hands it to me. 'I found it on the floor in Costa as I was leaving.'

'Oh, that's brilliant, thank you so much. You've totally saved my life!'

'I'm sorry I couldn't get it back to you before. I knew you'd be worried but I had the boys this afternoon, so . . . and I didn't have your landline number or I'd have called you.'

'Honestly, don't worry about that – I'm just glad to have it back. I didn't even realise it was missing until about an hour ago. Look, come in for a bit. Simon's just got home.'

Simon is smiling. 'Nice to see you, Anna, and well done for spotting it.'

I'm sure I see his eyes flicker appreciatively over her body. She's wearing skinny jeans with a little red cotton top that hangs loosely around her taut midriff.

'It was under the table.' She turns to me. 'Must have fallen out of your bag when you picked it up.'

Simon shakes his head, then turns to Anna. 'Would you like a drink, Anna? Wine? Or are you driving?'

'No, my car's playing up. Only starts when it feels like it.' She looks at her watch. 'A quick glass of wine would be lovely.' She smiles that smile of hers, then she looks at me. 'That's if I'm not interrupting . . . I mean, were you about to have your dinner?'

'No, not for a good half hour.' I turn to Simon. 'I've taken a pizza out of the freezer. I was going to message you to ask you to pick up some salad on your way home. That's when I realised I didn't have my phone.'

'Tell you what, then, let's all have a drink, and then I can give Anna a lift back when I pop out for the salad.'

'That's okay,' Anna says. 'I can walk. It's fine – I like walking.'

'No, you were good enough to come over with Emily's phone. I insist.'

We sit out on the terrace and spend a pleasant half hour or so drinking wine and chatting, mainly about the little boys Anna's been looking after and how sad she is that they're moving, and how their mum had given her flowers and chocolates and they'd both made her sweet little cards. We don't talk about the possibility of her looking after Bonnie, but I can tell Simon is relaxing more with her now.

'Your garden's amazing,' Anna says. 'It's massive!'

It's a good size, but it's not that big. I suppose we take it for granted.

'You're so lucky to have all this, Emily.' Anna looks right into my eyes as she says this, and for some reason, I find myself shifting under her gaze. She doesn't talk much about her childhood, but I know there wasn't much money around, so this must seem like luxury.

'I know. We're very lucky to live here. It's largely thanks to our parents – we'd never have been able to afford the deposit on our own.'

Anna nods enigmatically and doesn't say any more.

'You've been a long time,' I say when Simon comes back from dropping her home.

'Yes,' he says, tossing the bag of salad leaves onto the

worktop. 'She lives further away than I expected — a good couple of miles.'

'Really? Doesn't she live . . .' But I realise Anna hasn't said exactly where she lives, just that it's a grotty flat on a not very nice road. 'I assumed she lived about ten minutes' walk away.'

Simon nods towards Oscar, who's sitting on top of the fridge, washing himself. 'That cat must have been on quite an adventure if she found him near her place.' He chuckles. 'Either that or he was trying to run away.'

CHAPTER THIRTEEN

It's a lovely day, definitely warm enough to eat outside, and now I'm wishing I'd gone for the sort of 'picky' lunch we often have at weekends during the summer. Simon pops down to Waitrose for a loaf of sourdough and some bits and pieces from the deli counter – cheese, salami, hummus, olives, maybe a couple of those mini quiches if they have them. Then we crack open a bottle of Rioja and just graze while we sit out on the terrace, watching Bonnie play on the grass. But I remembered Anna mentioning how much she loved a 'proper Sunday dinner', so I decided to do roast chicken with all the trimmings, and now I'm regretting it. The phrase *slaving over a hot stove* jumps into my mind as I run my hand under the cold tap and splash water on my overheated face. As I baste the roast potatoes, I wonder what possessed me to attempt what is essentially an only slightly toned-down version of Christmas dinner, which I've never actually cooked. Last year was the first time I didn't have Christmas dinner at my mum's – she decided to spend Christmas in France with her friend from the wine-tasting group. And there was me worrying that she might be upset that we wouldn't want to spend the whole Christmas with her. But it was nice spending Bonnie's first Christmas here, with just us. The cooking didn't really count, though, because I bought everything ready prepared from Marks & Spencer. I glance at the clock. It's almost one. I need to finish the tiramisu, prepare the carrots and broccoli, lay the table and I'm more or less there. Shit! Stuffing! I was going to try and make my own, but I totally forgot to buy the ingredients. 'Simon,' I call through into the sitting room where he's watching cartoons with Bonnie. 'Can you pop round to Sainsbury's for a packet of stuffing mix?'

'Sure,' he calls back. He comes into the kitchen, Bonnie toddling along behind him. 'Shall I take her with me?'

'Yes, but take the pushchair. There isn't time for her to walk – I need it ASAP.' A minute or two later, I can hear Bonnie protesting as Simon straps her into the push-chair. 'And can you put her down for her nap when you get back?'

While Simon's out, I rush upstairs to run a cold washcloth over my face, neck and under my arms before changing my top and freshening my make-up. I pay special attention to my scar, because it always seems to look redder when I get hot, and the make-up wears off more quickly. First I use concealer, then I brush on a little powder, then more concealer, followed by a dab of foundation and a final dusting of powder. Finally, I dab jasmine oil inside my wrists and behind my ears.

As I walk downstairs, I meet Simon coming up with a sleeping Bonnie in his arms. When he comes back down, I ask him to lay the table. 'Use the good glasses. And can you uncork that, please.' I hand him a bottle of Médoc from the wine rack.

'Okay.' He takes the corkscrew from the drawer. 'You're going to an awful lot of trouble for this woman,' he comments.

I feel my hackles rise. 'Why shouldn't I?'

'No reason. Just saying.'

'She's become a good friend.' It's only as I'm saying this that I realise how true it is. I feel closer to Anna than I've felt to any of my other friends for a long time. I can *talk* to Anna.

'I know you like her, but it's as if you're trying to impress her.' Then he grins. 'Do you fancy her or something?'

Do I? No, it's definitely not that. I grin back. 'Only in your fantasies.'

'Ah well, a man can dream . . .'

'Do *you* fancy her, then?'

He laughs, even though I'm not sure I'm joking. 'I don't need to change, do I?' he says, looking down at the loose white shirt he's wearing over his jeans.

'You're fine. Don't change the subject – do you fancy her?' I'm keeping my tone light, wondering why I'm even asking, although I did notice him looking at her the other night when she popped round with my phone. And Lisa's words in the staffroom last week keep popping back into my head. *Once a cheater, always a cheater.*

'Not my type,' he says, and I know immediately that the waft of relief I feel is stupid because he would say that, wouldn't he? 'Though she's quite attractive when she smiles,' he adds mischievously. 'Nice eyes, too.'

'You used to say I had nice eyes.'

'You do ...' He slides his arms around my waist from behind and nuzzles my neck. 'You have gorgeous eyes.'

I rest my head against his, comforted by the feel of his lips on my neck. His hands move upwards. 'Nice tits, too. What time's she getting here?'

I look up at the clock. It's bang on one. 'Shit. I said half past one – we've got half an hour.'

'That's time for a quickie.'

I laugh and shrug him off. 'I've still got to do the stuffing and finish the tiramasu.'

'You're no fun anymore,' he says, but he's smiling as he starts to put out the wine glasses.

I've almost finished whipping the cream when the doorbell goes. 'Who on earth's that?' I shout over the sound of the electric whisk. 'Get rid of them, will you? I've got to get this finished.'

As I turn the whisk off, I hear Simon say, 'Anna! Very glam! Come on in – we're in the kitchen.' It's five past one. How bizarre to turn up twenty-five minutes early! I'm rinsing my hands as Anna appears in the doorway, holding a bottle of wine. I do a double-take. She looks stunning, hair pinned up in a loose bun, wispy tendrils framing her face and drawing attention to the dangly silver earrings. She's wearing a cherry-red sleeveless sheath dress, which shows off her neat little figure to perfection. 'Anna, you look fabulous!' I give her a hug, which she returns, slightly awkwardly. 'You smell nice, too.'

'Thank you.' Anna smiles modestly. 'It's jasmine oil. It smelled so nice on you, I thought I'd try it myself.'

'Well, snap!' I smile. They say imitation is the sincerest form of flattery.

'That for us?' Simon says, nodding towards the wine.

'Oh, sorry, yes.' She hands the bottle to Simon and rummages in her bag. 'I bought some chocolates, too.'

'Aww, that's nice of you. No need, but thank you.'

'Lambrusco,' Simon says, furtively giving me a look of mock horror. 'I'll put it in the fridge.'

'It'll go perfectly with the tiramisu.' I smile. 'Have a seat, Anna. I'm—'

'Sorry I'm a few minutes late,' Anna says. 'The clock in my flat is slow and I keep forgetting.'

'You're not late.' I laugh. 'We said half past, so you're actually a bit early. We're not quite ready yet, but it'll be—'

Anna's nodding. 'Yeah, you said half one at first, but then you WhatsApped me to say could we make it one. Something about fitting in with Bonnie's nap. At least,' she starts to rummage in her bag, 'I think that's what you said.'

She's got it wrong, but it's no big deal. 'Never mind.' I smile. 'It's not a problem. Simon'll get you a drink while I do the last bits towards lunch. Just don't watch me because I'm bound to cock it up.'

'There!' Anna holds her phone in front of me. And sure enough, there it is in black and white. Well, black and green. *Sorry, could we make Sunday lunch 1pm instead? Hopefully Bonnie will be napping, so it'll be easier. Emily xx* And there's a smiley emoji.

I stare at it, searching my memory in vain. 'I don't . . .' I start to shake my head, but I can feel both Anna and Simon watching me. 'Haha. Oh God, yes of course – totally forgot!'

But I have absolutely no recollection of sending that message. I must be losing the plot.

Over lunch, it's clear that Simon is warming to Anna. Possibly a little too much. Is he flirting? He's being very charming, but then he always is. Is Anna flirting? No, probably not. She's just politely laughing at his jokes.

By the time we've finished the main course, it's more or less decided: Anna will pick up Bonnie from Gemma's and look after her until one of us gets home, starting with one afternoon next week, two the week after, and if that works out, all three from then on.

As I clear the plates, I hear Anna ask Simon, 'So how did you two meet?'

'Through work,' Simon says. 'I'd already been at Woodview for a few years when Emily joined the school as head of English.'

Anna's listening attentively. 'So, did you get together straight away?'

'More or less,' I say, coming back to the table with the dessert dishes. 'He introduced himself on my first day, and about a week later someone had a birthday and invited the whole Humanities department to the pub. Simon and I ended up sitting next to each other and we just hit it off.'

'Ah, lovely. Was the school all right about it? I mean, some places don't like their staff going out with each other, do they?'

Simon and I exchange a look. 'It's okay if you're discreet,' he says.

Anna nods. 'You didn't have to keep it secret or anything?'

'Well, we didn't exactly shout it from the rooftops.' I feel a nasty twist in my stomach as I remember Simon telling me not to tell anyone, to wait until they got to know me a bit better, and me innocently believing he was saying that for my sake.

'Anyway,' Simon gets to his feet, 'let's have pudding. Is it in the fridge, Em?'

'Stay there,' I say. 'I'll get it.' I can't quite face the Lambrusco with the tiramisu, so I pretend it's not chilled enough and I fetch the bottle of Sauternes I'd planned to serve originally. Simon is now chatting animatedly to Anna, so he's drinking more slowly than usual, and when I reach for the bottle to top up my glass, he turns his attention away from Anna momentarily to mutter, 'Slow down, Em.'

CHAPTER FOURTEEN

The new arrangement works well. Bonnie's happy, and I'm finally getting on top of my lesson planning. Anna is amazing! Not only does she look after Bonnie and cook her a proper meal when they get back from Gemma's, but she does other bits and pieces as well. By the time I got home on Tuesday, she'd cleaned the kitchen and defrosted the freezer, and then last night she suggested I give her a shopping list so she could go to Sainsbury's after picking Bonnie up. When I got home, the cupboards, fridge and freezer were full, so that's another job I don't have to worry about.

Today, I have a free period straight after lunch. I could spend it getting all my preparation out of the way; I could be home by five and have the whole evening free. But it's a beautiful sunny day, warm enough to go bare-armed, and as I now don't have to be home until six thirty or even seven, I decide to go for a walk, maybe sit in the park and read. I'm fairly sure Simon has a free period after lunch too, so maybe we could drive somewhere and have a proper lunch in a cafe. There are plenty of places to eat within walking distance but we'd be too likely to bump into pupils.

When the pips go at the end of period four, there's the usual scramble and scraping of chairs. 'Wait!' I shout. 'The sound of the pips is *not* the signal for you to rampage out of this room. Sit down again until you're dismissed. I said *sit!*' It took me a few years to get to the point where I could get a group to listen, and mostly now, they do. But there's always a terrifying moment when I think they might not comply this time, and if you've lost them once, you've lost them for ever. They pull out their chairs and sit back down. They look pissed off, and some of them are sitting sideways, still holding their bags and rucksacks ready for a quick getaway. But they *are* sitting. 'Thank you,' I say, more quietly. 'Okay, off you go and have your lunch. See you next time.'

I click on WhatsApp and message Simon: *You free period 5? Fancy going somewhere nice for lunch?* When I've tidied my stuff away, I sling my bag over my shoulder, pick up my keys and check my phone, but the two ticks on the message are still grey – he hasn't seen it. After locking the classroom, I make my way upstairs to his office, but the door's locked, so I try the staff room. He's not there either. It's ten minutes since the end of period four, so he can't still be teaching. 'Anyone seen Simon?'

'He was in here first thing,' Rachel, one of the new supply teachers, replies, 'but I haven't seen him since.' A few other people look up, but no-one says anything.

'Okay, thanks.' I check my phone again. There's a missed

call from a private number. My breath catches. It's been weeks since I had one of those silent calls, so I thought they'd stopped. I stare at my phone for a second, then I tell myself it's a coincidence. I open WhatsApp, but Simon still hasn't seen the message. The staff room is definitely a friendlier place now than it was before I went on maternity leave. Probably because there are so many new teaching staff who, presumably, haven't heard about my fiancé-stealing status. I try calling, but it rings and then goes to voicemail so it's probably on silent. Next, I try the Humanities office. There are a few people in there, inputting data at the computers, but no Simon. Maybe he's been held up by a pupil, or he's standing in a corridor somewhere, chatting with a colleague. It's now fifteen minutes into lunchtime and I can already feel my free time disappearing, plus the headache that has been threatening all morning is starting to kick in now. After another quick look in the staff room, I head down the stairs and out of the building. As I walk, the image of Simon and Sarah chatting in front of the noticeboard a few weeks back jumps into my mind again, and that's when it occurs to me that Sarah wasn't in the staff room or the Humanities office either. Maybe they're together, in Sarah's office? I'm sure there are things they legitimately need to discuss, something school-related. Or maybe they're having a friendly chat, having gone from not speaking at all in those hideous weeks when it first came out, to just being civil, to giggling together. Could it be more than that? Suddenly, I picture them, naked, on the floor of her office – or his. Up against the wall, Sarah's slim legs wrapped around him; or him sitting on the chair, Sarah astride him. *Stop it,* I tell myself. *Just stop it.*

I've walked as far as the Sainsbury's Local. I need to pick up a few bits anyway and the ten minutes or so I spend shopping distract me from thinking about Simon and Sarah, but I vaguely wonder whether I'd be able to find him if I were to go back to school now. A glance at my phone shows that he still hasn't seen the WhatsApp message. I chuck a sandwich and a bottle of water into my basket with the other bits and, vaguely registering a couple of pupils in the self-checkout queue, I scan my shopping, pay and then head off to the park. It takes me a while to focus on what I'm reading, and I'm starting to lose myself in the story when a message comes through. *Only just seen this, so bit late to join you. Need to grab a bite, then safeguarding meeting in ten minutes. Soz! See you later x*

Resisting the temptation to ask where he was earlier, I reply, *Ok x.* As I walk back to school, I have to make a conscious effort to stop thinking about him and get my head together for periods six and seven.

This Year 9 group can be challenging at the best of times, and as soon as they pour into the classroom, I can tell they're not going to be easy this afternoon. This is all I need. It's hard enough dealing with a difficult class when you're on top of everything, but being distracted and having a thumping headache make it a nightmare. The group is fidgety and restless. There's talking, giggling and checking of phones. They're pushing me to see what they can get away with. If

I was on the ball, I'd be threatening detentions now, but I don't have the mental energy, and I can't stop thinking about Simon and Sarah and what they may or may not have been doing this lunchtime.

I push these thoughts to the back of my mind and concentrate on handling the class. But I struggle to keep my temper and I end up shouting at them. Stupid. Shouting only makes things worse, and if I'm honest, it's not so much their behaviour that's getting to me, it's Simon's. I'm trying to convince myself that my imagination is working overtime, that of course there isn't anything going on, and if there was, it certainly wouldn't be happening on school premises. But then again, the first time he kissed me we were in my office in the middle of the school day. The rational part of my brain thinks, why would Sarah be interested in him again after what happened? But another part knows she seems to have forgiven him. Or maybe she sees it as justifiable revenge on me. There are some times when I feel so certain they're seeing each other, I start asking myself why *wouldn't* he want her instead of me? She's beautiful, tall, slim, successful – and she's not sleep-deprived and distracted by teething and nappies. And I remember how, when he fell in love with me, he insisted he couldn't help himself, like it was out of his control.

Once a cheater, always a cheater.

Some of the kids are looking at me intently, scrutinising me. They can see I'm distracted and they know something's up. I turn away and pick up the whiteboard marker. 'Okay, so your homework for this week ...' As I'm writing on the whiteboard, there's a sudden change in the atmosphere, one or two muted sniggers. I sense movement and turn to face them, and that's when I spot a note being passed around. 'All right,' I say, marching to the back of the classroom and holding my hand out. 'Give it to me, please.'

'I didn't write it, Miss,' Lily Robinson says, handing it over. 'I ain't even read it.'

'All right, Lily.' I walk back to the front of the room, ignoring the sniggers behind me. Usually, I'd just chuck the note in a drawer and look at it later, but for some reason, I stand in front of the classroom and I unfold the paper right there and then.

Know why she's being such a COW? It reads. *Saw her in Sainsbury's at lunchtime, getting TAMPAX + FEMINAX + CHOCOLATE BISCITS!!! PMT ALERT! PMT ALERT!*

I feel the blood draining from my skin. Why did I decide to read it in front of them? Stupid, stupid, stupid. I am suddenly ultra-aware of myself, as though I can feel every cell of my body, from the fingertips touching the paper I'm holding to the dampness under my armpits to the flesh of my feet where the straps of my sandals are cutting in. What do I do now? Toss it in a drawer anyway and give them all detention? I read the note again. *Chocolate biscits.* A misspelling or a slip of the pen? I don't stand a chance of recognising the handwriting, but there are a few poor spellers in this group. I scan the faces. It's a risk, but I'd lay money on Skye Harris, Hayden Smith or Molly Weston. 'Right, a little impromptu spelling test, I think.' There's a collective groan. 'Don't worry,' I say.

'Only two words. Back of your exercise books, please.' I walk slowly around the class as they turn to the back of their books. 'Okay, I'd like you all to write the words *chocolate biscuits*. In capital letters, please. That's all you need to do. Quickly now.' Those who've seen the note aren't stupid, they know what I'm doing. But there are a few bewildered faces. I stroll around the tables, heart pounding, as I look over shoulders. If I get this wrong . . . Hayden's and Skye's are both spelt correctly. I am holding my breath as I get to Molly. 'Molly, come along, it's only two words. What's the hold-up?'

'It's stupid, Miss. What's the point?'

I tap the blank page in her book with my finger. 'Never mind that. Capital letters, please.'

Molly sighs and shifts in her chair. 'I don't see why we have to just write two words; that's not a spelling test.'

'Okay then, come and see me at three twenty and I'll give you more words.' A snort of laughter from the class. 'But I'd still like you to write these two now, please.'

She sighs again and, scowling, picks up her pen and writes *CHOCOLATE BISCITS*.

I almost laugh with relief as I stroll back to the front of the room. 'Molly,' I say in the calmest voice I can muster, 'I'd like you to stay behind after the lesson, please.' And to the rest of the class who are starting to mutter, I speak louder, sharper: 'And anyone who has an opinion can stay behind as well. Clear?' They nod and murmur assent. It's only a few minutes until the pips go and that's taken up with them copying the homework into their exercise books.

Molly saunters up to me after the class has been dismissed. 'Am I getting a sanction, then?' she says, chewing gum.

'Will your parents be in this evening? Say between,' I look at my watch, 'six and nine?'

The girl looks up sharply. 'Why do you want to know? You're not going to call them, are you?'

'Well, let's see. Why do you think I might want to talk to your parents?'

She casts her eyes down.

'Any ideas?' I unfold the note again and place it in front of her. Her eyes flicker towards it and then away again. She has the decency to look embarrassed, and mumbles something under her breath.

'What was that, Molly?'

'I said, *sorry Miss.*'

'Thank you.'

Molly bites her lip. 'Do you have to call them?' she says quietly.

'We'll have to see, won't we?' I pick up the paper and pen. 'Okay, Molly, you can go now.'

I know I won't need to call her parents, and she probably knows it, too. It's unlikely that Molly Weston will be any more trouble this term, but this is a wake-up call. I've made two stupid mistakes today – one, losing my temper and shouting at them, and two, reading that note in front of them. I've allowed my personal problems to affect me in class and once you do that, you risk losing everything you've built up. I seem to have got away with it this time, but only just.

CHAPTER FIFTEEN

I'm irritable and preoccupied after the run-in with Molly and although I get a little marking done before I go home, I can't concentrate so I end up leaving just after five and taking a couple of batches with me. Maybe I can get up early and get some of it out of the way first thing tomorrow.

When I get home, I flop down on the kitchen sofa and tell Anna what a shitty rotten day I've had. 'Looks like you could do with a glass of wine,' she says. 'Shall I pour you one?'

'Oh yes please. It's very nearly wine o'clock. And anyway, it's Thursday, which means it's basically Friday.' I manage a big smile as Bonnie toddles over, holding out her toy phone. 'Is it for me?'

'Deh.' Bonnie nods.

'Who is it? Is it Daddy?'

Bonnie grins and nods again. 'Deh.' She gets the game now, whereas she used to look around for Simon whenever he was mentioned.

'Hello, Daddy,' I say. 'What's that? You'd like to talk to Bonnie? Okay, here she is.' When I hand it back, Bonnie puts it to her ear and nods and chatters into it, an earnest expression on her face.

Anna smiles as she takes an unopened bottle of Pinot from the fridge, then opens the cupboard where the glasses are kept and stands on tiptoe to take one down from the shelf.

'Grab one for yourself,' I say. 'After all, it's your Friday too.'

'Not really,' Anna says. 'I'm at the pub for the next three nights.' She glances up at the clock. 'But thanks, I'll have a small one.'

'Sorry, I forget you slog your guts out all weekend as well as looking after Madam here.' Moving from the sofa to the kitchen table, I pick Bonnie up and pull her onto my lap, kissing her blonde curls and blowing a raspberry into her sweaty little neck. She squeals and giggles. 'You must be knackered before you even start.'

'Oh, she's no trouble at all, are you, chick?'

'Deh,' Bonnie says, sliding off my lap and then toddling back to her toybox. As I watch Anna reach into the second drawer for the corkscrew, closing it again with her hip, I notice how at ease she is in my kitchen, how confidently she occupies the space, knowing which cupboards and drawers to go to, knowing exactly where to find things.

Anna pours a large glass for me and a smaller measure for herself, then brings them to the table. As she sits down, I think I get a whiff of cigarette smoke, but then I'm not sure.

'So come on,' she says. 'Why has it been a shitty day?'

At first, I simply relate the incident with Molly, but then I find myself telling her about not being able to find Simon at lunchtime. 'I know I'm probably being paranoid, but it's just that she and Simon used to be together, and I suppose at the back of my mind, I wonder whether there's still anything there.'

Anna's eyes widen. 'Really? He used to go out with this Sarah and she works at the same school?'

'Yes. And what makes it worse is that they're both assistant heads, so they're in meetings together all the time.'

Anna nods. 'Hmm. I can see why you're not over the moon about that. How long ago did he go out with her anyway? Before he met you, I mean?'

My gaze falls to my wine glass. 'That's where it gets complicated.' I sigh, and take a fortifying drink before I tell her the whole story – the instant attraction, how we both wanted the same things, and how we were six weeks into a relationship before he told me about Sarah.

Anna listens in silence, nodding from time to time until I finish, then she lets out a breath as a long, slow whistle. 'I see what you mean.'

'And yes, before you ask, I felt guilty as fuck. I still do. I suppose I should have ended it as soon as I found out, but by that time I was in love, and we'd planned a future together, kids, a proper family.'

'How did she react, this Sarah?'

'Oh, she was very grown up about it, according to Simon. No histrionics or anything. Apparently she just quietly took her key to his flat off her key ring, put it on the table, then asked for her own key back. She didn't speak to either of us for months, which was totally fair enough.' I almost shudder at the memory. 'A few of the other teachers stopped speaking to me, although that didn't seem to happen to Simon as much. It was a shitty thing to do though, wasn't it? Taking another woman's fiancé?'

'Bollocks,' Anna says, with a vehemence that surprises me. 'You can't "take" a man who doesn't want to be taken. Going by what you're saying, *he* was the one who made the first move; *he* was the one who was engaged, and *he* was the one who lied – to both of you. And you're the one who's taking all the blame!' She picks up the wine bottle and tops up my glass. 'No wonder you need a drink!'

'Aren't you having another?'

Anna shakes her head. 'Driving.'

'I know he isn't blameless.' *Once a cheater, always a cheater.* 'But it's that thing about women being supportive to each other, isn't it? I think that's why some of the other female teachers were so off with me. A couple of my mates, too. You don't *do* that to another woman.'

Anna leans forward and takes my wrist in her hand. 'You didn't "do" that to another woman. You didn't even know he was going out with someone, let alone that he was engaged.'

'I know, but when I *did* find out—'

'But he was going to split up with her anyway!'

I stop, glass halfway to my mouth. 'How did you know that?'

Anna sips her wine. 'You said. You said he was going to split up with her anyway because she didn't want kids.'

'Did I? I don't remember saying that.'

'I don't mean just now. It was a while ago.' Her hand creeps up to her locket. 'I think it was that day we went for that nice lunch when I'd only known you a few weeks. We were talking about Bonnie and you told me that Simon had always wanted kids and that it was one of the reasons you two got together. You said he'd split up with his previous girlfriend because she didn't want kids. I just put two and two together. It *was* her that didn't want kids, wasn't it? Or was that another girlfriend?'

'No, it was her. Sorry, I forgot I'd mentioned it.' I still don't remember telling her that, but I suppose I must have done. It *was* a boozy lunch, and I do tend to overshare when I'm drinking.

'I'm sure you've got nothing to worry about,' Anna continues, topping up my glass again. 'I suppose it's a bit weird that you couldn't find him today, but at least with you working at the same school, you can keep an eye on the pair of them. Anyway,' she glances up at the clock, 'I'd better get going.' She finishes her wine, then takes her glass to the sink to wash it.

'Don't worry about that, Anna. Leave it there and I'll stick it in the dishwasher later.'

'It won't take a minute,' she says, carefully washing the glass, drying it, and putting it back in the cupboard before picking up her bag and bending down to kiss Bonnie.

'See you next week, then,' Anna says, walking towards the door. 'Doing anything nice over the weekend?'

'No big plans,' I reply. 'You?'

She smiles. 'I'm working lunchtimes as well this weekend. Hard going, but I can't afford to turn it down.' Then she waves and is gone, leaving me feeling slightly unsettled. I'm not sure if it's guilt because Anna has to work long shifts in a pub to make ends meet or if it's something to do with her knowing that detail about Sarah that I really can't remember telling her.

I'd fully intended to cook tonight, but I haven't got time now so I take a couple of chicken jalfrezis out of the freezer, then I take Bonnie upstairs to get her ready for bed. We're back down and sitting on the sofa reading a story when Simon comes home. I see him look pointedly at my empty wine glass. 'I had a quick drink with Anna before she left. It's been a shit day.'

His eyes flicker to the table, then over to the sink. 'Okay,' he says, in that *if you say so* sort of way, and it's only later, when we're loading the dishwasher after supper, that I realise Simon thinks I've been drinking alone, but if I press the point that I wasn't, it'll look even worse. Not that I shouldn't have a glass of wine on my own after work if I want one.

CHAPTER SIXTEEN

Although it isn't 'flaming June' until tomorrow, it's sweltering today and according to the weather forecast, it's going to stay like this for a while. It's hard to make myself stay here in this stuffy classroom, ploughing through a stack of exercise books when all I want to do is go home and sit in the garden. I've spent so much time creating new resources this week that the marking's built up so I really need to stay and get on with it. Simon reckons he'll be home by seven, and I'm not going to be back much before that, so I message Anna to ask if she'd mind staying a bit later. *One of us will definitely be there by 7.15,* I tell her. *Would that be okay?*

She replies straight away. *No worries. We're in the garden – I'm working on my tan, Bonnie covered in sunblock! Shed was open so I took one of the sun loungers out. Hope you don't mind? Also, saw the mower so I thought I'd cut the grass while Bonnie was napping – I remember you saying it needed doing. Anything I can do towards your dinner?*

Anna, you are a legend! I type back. *We'll get pizza tonight — stay and join us!*

That would be lovely, she replies. *Thanks!*

I'm still marking when Simon puts his head around the door. 'How are you doing? Meeting's postponed until tomorrow, so I'm done for today.'

I nod towards the pile of books I still have to get through. 'I've got to get this lot finished tonight.' I look up at the clock. 'I'll be about another half hour.'

'Okay. I'll head home and relieve Anna, then. What are we eating? Do you want me to pick anything up?'

I tell him about Anna cutting the grass and that I've invited her to join us for pizza. He nods. 'Okay. See you there in a bit, then.'

It's gone half past six but it's still incredibly hot and the air con has packed up so the car's like an oven. When I'm twenty minutes away, I call Simon to ask if he'll get Bonnie ready for bed because I want to dive straight in the shower when I get in. 'Already done!' he says. 'It's a bit early, but she was yawning her head off so we've given her a bath and she's in her cot now. Anna's reading her a story.'

We. 'Oh, okay. I was going to read her a story when I got in.'

'I thought you wanted to jump straight in the shower?'

'Yes, but after. I mean—'

'Well anyway, it's all under control. She'll probably be asleep by the time you get here — she's knackered. She's been "helping" Anna in the garden, apparently, and they've had the hose out, so she's had a great time.' I can hear the smile in his voice. It's always there when he talks about Bonnie. I want to say no, don't let her go to sleep, keep her awake so I can kiss her goodnight, but I know that's selfish so instead I tell him to give her a kiss for me, and I ask him to order the pizza in about ten minutes. I picture Bonnie toddling around after Anna, like she does with me, her little face full of the importance of being a special helper. Childishly, I find myself thinking, *but she's supposed to be* my *special helper.*

I let myself in quietly. Even though I wanted to say good-night to Bonnie, I don't want to disturb her. I can't hear any sound from upstairs, so I assume she's asleep. I poke my head around the kitchen door. 'Hello. Did she go down okay?'

Simon nods. 'Out like a light.' He's changed into denim cut-offs and a white T-shirt, and his Ray-Bans are pushed up onto the top of his head. He looks like he's just stepped out of the pages of a catalogue as he pours wine into two glasses.

'Thanks,' I say, 'but I'm going to jump in the shower first.'

'Okay.' He picks up the glasses. 'We're in the garden.' Of course. The second glass is for Anna. 'Don't be too long,' he says. 'Pizza should be here in ten minutes.'

It seems even hotter now than it was at lunchtime. Usually, I'd go straight to the en suite, but instead, I decide to use the main bathroom. I peel my sweaty clothes off and turn the shower on, but before I get in, I peek out of the bathroom window, which overlooks the terrace. Simon is standing, glass in hand, smiling as he talks to Anna, who is lying stretched out on the sun lounger, showing off her perfectly proportioned non-baby figure. She's wearing a pretty turquoise strapless bikini, which is fastened at the bust with a bow. I can't help but wonder why she brought a bikini with her. Her bikini bottoms have ties at either side. Simon's wearing his sunglasses again now, so I can't see the look on his face, but even I think she looks like a pretty little gift, waiting to be unwrapped. She's holding her hand up to shield her eyes from the low glare of the evening sun. With the sound of the shower running in the background, I can't hear what they're saying, but they're both smiling, and then he says something that makes her laugh. She slides one of her legs up so it's bent at the knee. God, is she flirting with him? Is he flirting with her? Then I answer my own question – of course he is. Simon can't help but flirt with attractive women. But is she flirting with him? And is it a bit cheeky, planning to sunbathe while she's looking after my daughter? Or am I being mean? She's a friend, I tell myself. Even though I'm paying her, it's not like she's working for me. Maybe it's not that weird.

After my shower, I pad into the bedroom and pull on my old denim shorts, sending up a silent prayer that I can still get them done up – which I can, but only just. I put on the white cotton camisole top I bought from Next last week. Normally, I wouldn't bother with putting make-up on again, but next to Anna, I feel big and frumpy and pale, so I re-do the concealer on my scar, add a touch of eyeshadow and mascara, and the tiniest smear of lip colour. I'm about to go back downstairs when I notice the little drawer in my jewellery box is open, which is odd, because it's where I keep my earrings and I've not used it for a while. I've been wearing the same pair of pearl studs for the last few days so I've been leaving them on the bedside table. Straightaway, I realise that the big silver hoops are missing. They're too big to wear at school, so the last time I wore them would have been a weekend. A week or two ago, maybe? I check on my dressing table, and in the en suite, but there's no sign of them, and anyway, I always put them back in that drawer. I don't know why I didn't notice it was open this morning. Surely, Anna wouldn't . . . I feel guilty for even thinking it, and I dismiss the thought immediately. If Anna was going to nick a pair of earrings, she wouldn't leave the drawer wide open, would she?

By the time I join them in the garden, Anna's dressed again, thank goodness. She's wearing a long, diaphanous purple skirt with a white camisole top that's identical to mine. 'Looks like we've been to the same shop,' I say, conscious that it looks better on her. Mine is a size 14, but I'm guessing hers is a 10.

'Yes.' Anna beams. 'Next. I told you I was thinking of buying one the same, remember?'

I'm aware that I'm looking at her blankly. 'No, I don't, actually. I didn't realise I'd even shown it to you.'

She laughs. 'Well, you definitely did. You showed me it on Monday, said you'd bought it on Saturday. And I said, I've been looking for something like that for a while, and you said they still had a few of them in Next.'

I did buy it on Saturday, but I'm absolutely certain I didn't show it to her. 'Are you sure? I really don't remember—'

'Never mind,' Simon interrupts. 'You both have the same top, you both look gorgeous, what does it matter?'

Before I can say anything else, Simon gets the notification on his phone that the pizza is here.

We eat outside and the scorching day softens into a still, balmy evening. It's pleasant, sitting out here, but I find I'm watching Simon closely, noticing how often he looks at Anna, noticing how he laughs every time she says anything even remotely amusing. Then I'm thinking about Sarah again, and how well she seems to have got over her perfectly justified animosity towards Simon. And it really bothers me, because if I'd been her, I don't think I'd even be speaking to him.

CHAPTER SEVENTEEN

The dream doesn't have much of a narrative, it's more of a sensation. I'm in a small space, unable to move and feeling claustrophobic and frightened, though I'm not sure what I'm frightened of. I'm crying, really sobbing, and desperately trying to free myself. It's as though something is physically restraining me so that I can't move my arms. But then Anna is there, and I'm not sure if she's trying to free me or if she's holding my wrists so tightly that I can't move. Something terrible has happened and I can feel the panic rising. I try to scream.

I'm drenched in sweat when I wake, my throat aching with the effort of trying to produce a scream while sleeping. The sense of panic ebbs away as my eyes adjust to the early morning sunlight slicing through the curtains. It's only twenty to six so I turn over and pull the duvet up to block out the light, but the dream has left me with a feeling of gloom and I can't seem to shake it off. I doze for a while but

I'm clearly not going to get back to sleep, which is annoying, given that I'm not in school today.

I've just settled Bonnie in her highchair with some cubed cheese and apple wedges when a text comes through from Anna. *Coffee this afternoon?*

I text back: *Sorry – meant to mention last week. Frantically busy today. Loads to do this morning, then lunch with my mum, then dentist at 3. And I MUST to do some marking! So much for my day off! Sorry! BTW, re picnic – how about next week? (today's out, obvs, and they're servicing the boiler on Friday) Mon or Fri next week. Whatever works for you xxx*

A minute or so later, Anna's reply comes through: *I can do Friday* No little exes, no emoji, not even an exclamation mark. Maybe she's busy.

The day flies by. We go swimming first – Bonnie loves the 'ducklings' session. Then it's on to toddler yoga before we go to my mum's for lunch, an invitation that only came after I mentioned my dental appointment. I suspect she thought it was 'safe' to suggest lunch at one, knowing we'd be on our way again by half past two.

When we arrive, I'm touched to see that she's gone to the trouble of making a miniature pasta, cheese and broccoli bake for Bonnie. 'It's too hot to eat outside,' she says, taking the tiny dish out of the oven. 'So I thought we'd eat in the conservatory, then at least we got the blinds to keep the sun off.' She takes off her apron and hangs it on a hook behind the door. 'Do go through, darling. Everything's ready.'

The handmade wooden highchair is set up, and the box of toys she keeps in the utility room is in the middle of the floor. Our meals are laid out on the table – smoked salmon and asparagus quiche with spinach and rocket salad, and there's panna cotta and fresh raspberries to follow. It'll all have been ordered from the artisan baker's-cum-deli down the road. There's a bottle of Prosecco chilling in the ice bucket, and for a moment, I wonder whether I'd be safe to drive after half a bottle of Prosecco; after all, it's only 11 per cent, and if I were to drink it slowly . . . But then I remember I've got the dentist this afternoon, so I can't linger.

Tall, elegant, and still slim and attractive at seventy-one, my mother likes to eat well and never seems to gain an ounce. I always feel dumpy and clumsy beside her, as though I've never quite been able to be the daughter she hoped I'd be.

As always, she asks the same old questions over lunch – *how is Simon?* (She likes Simon.) *Is he still enjoying his new role? Has he thought any more about taking up golf?* (Simon hates golf, but when my mother asks, he pretends he's considering it, which means she'll keep bloody asking.) Then she asks me how I'm 'getting on', but I learned long ago that she isn't particularly interested in hearing about school or teaching. And she certainly doesn't want to talk about anything that actually matters. But she keeps asking the same vague questions, or trying to engage me with 'safe' topics – films or TV shows, restaurants, gossip about neighbours or her ex-fellow magistrates – because as long as she can fill the time with superficial chatter, there's less opportunity for me to ask those questions she doesn't want to answer.

At least she seems more interested in Bonnie now, and today, when Bonnie toddles over and plonks a Peppa Pig board book on her knees, she actually pulls her onto her lap and reads her the story.

Perhaps it's ungenerous of me, but it flits through my mind that she might only be reading to Bonnie to fill any spare moments during which I might raise the subject I'm not supposed to raise. I'm not going to start that conversation again today, but I'm not going to let it drop either. Before I had Bonnie, I asked her about my family history a few times, but she made it abundantly clear that it was something she didn't want to discuss. But now I have a daughter of my own, it's not just about me, it's about her too. So one day, whether my mother likes it or not, we *are* going to have that conversation.

I have to park a few minutes away from the dentist's and as I'm walking along the road, I see Zoe coming out of Boots. It's too late for me to duck out of sight because she's obviously seen me and is walking towards me. 'Hello, Emily,' she says. It's neither friendly, nor unfriendly. 'How are you?'

'I'm fine,' I say. 'You?' I assumed the fact that she never replied to my email meant that our friendship was definitely over, but I suppose that doesn't mean we have to ignore each other.

'Yeah, good.' Her tone is flat, and she's not meeting my eye. 'You didn't fancy meeting up, then?'

'Sorry?'

She looks at me. 'You didn't reply to my email.'

'Hang on, *I* didn't reply to *your* email? The way I remember it is, you didn't reply to mine.'

'I one hundred per cent did reply to yours! Not immediately – might have been a few days later because I was ridiculously busy.' She looks at her watch. 'I'm always bloody busy – but I definitely replied. I suggested we have lunch one day so we could talk about . . . well, everything.'

The relief is enormous. Things are clearly not the same between us, but at least she's still speaking to me. 'I never got it, Zo, or I'd have answered.'

Zoe looks at her watch again. 'I'm sorry, but I've got a meeting in twenty minutes. Look, are you free a week on Friday? It's the only day I'm free and it'll be the last chance for a while – I'm going to Greece that weekend.' She grins. 'For a year!'

'What? For a *year*?'

She nods. 'You remember I did that TEFL course? Well, I've got a year's contract teaching English in Thessaloniki. Look, I've really got to dash – can you make next Friday? I'll tell you all about it, then.'

'Wow! Yes, that Friday's fine.' As I say this, I remember that's the day Anna and I were going to have a picnic, but I'll suggest we do that on the Saturday instead.

'Cool. I'll message you,' Zoe says, giving Bonnie a wave before she hurries off along the road.

*

Bonnie's check-up goes well and she's entranced with the matching yellow toothbrush and sand timer set she receives from the dentist for being a good girl. She's still clutching it when we arrive home. I open the front door and set her down on the floor while I key the numbers into the burglar alarm. She heads straight for the stairs and immediately starts trying to climb them. When I lift her down, she cries and stamps her feet, shouting, 'Up! Up!' as she waves her new toothbrush and points up the stairs. 'All right, Bon-bon. We'll brush your teeth in a minute. Let Mummy put the kettle on first.' She looks doubtful. 'Just one little tiny baby minute, okay?'

'K,' Bonnie says.

In the kitchen, I kick my flip-flops off and walk barefoot over the sun-warmed wooden floor to open the window. Oscar rolls ecstatically in a patch of sunlight, exposing his soft white belly for me to rub. When I pick up the kettle to fill it, I'm surprised to find that it still feels warm. But no, it can't *still* be warm. I left before nine thirty this morning and it's now after four thirty. Simon must be back, although he didn't mention he'd be home early. I'm about to call up the stairs when I remember the burglar alarm was on when I came in, so he must have been in and gone out again. After I've filled the kettle and switched it on, I message him. *We're back. Where are you?* Then I take Bonnie up to the bathroom so she can use her new toothbrush.

Simon's reply comes through ten minutes later. *School, obvs! Should be able to get away in about an hour, so back by 6.30 hopefully. Anything wrong?*

I stare at the message. He *must* have been back. I open the dishwasher, but all that's in there is my own mug and plate and Bonnie's Peppa Pig bowl. The kettle stands opposite the main window, so perhaps it was warm from the sun pouring through the glass. I wish now that I hadn't boiled it so I could put my hand on it again, just to make sure. But no, I'm sure it was warm from being switched on, not from sitting in the sun. My stomach tightens as I remember how I couldn't find him at school that day last week. He's lying. He must be. Last night, as we were having supper, I told him everything I had to do today. I always do, because I'm convinced he thinks I spend Mondays and Fridays reclining on the sofa with a gin and tonic and watching daytime television. So he knew I'd be out all day.

I start opening cupboards and then closing them again, and I check the fridge but I can't see anything amiss. There's a film running in my head and I hate myself for allowing it, for creating it. Simon and Sarah, their free periods coinciding, a rare opportunity. Him standing close, his lips against her ear. *My house,* he whispers. *She'll be out all day.*

I'm trying to keep up the bright chatter as I settle Bonnie in her highchair with a banana, but inside, I feel sick. I prowl around the ground floor, eyes peeled, senses reaching out like invisible tentacles for anything different, any clue that Sarah's been here. Is that how I left the cushions on the sofa? Did I pull the curtains that far back this morning?

In the kitchen, Bonnie is happily singing a little song to herself.

'Just popping upstairs, sweetheart, okay?'

Bonnie nods. 'K.'

My stomach's doing somersaults as I climb the stairs. The sun is streaming through the stained-glass window on the landing, casting jewels of red, green and blue light onto the oatmeal carpet. I can feel the warmth on my bare arms as I pass, yet my hands feel like ice. I feel guilty for thinking what I'm thinking, and half of me is certain Simon wouldn't do such a thing, not in our house, in our bed. But the other half of me knows he's capable of blotting out uncomfortable truths if they get in the way. Otherwise, how could he have taken me back to his flat a week after we met, to a bed he'd shared with Sarah a few weeks earlier? When I asked him that question after it all came out, he said, 'It's not as if she *lived* there, is it?' Which suggested that if she *had* lived there, it wouldn't have happened. But now I'm not sure I believe that.

When I open the bedroom door, the first thing I'm aware of is the slight movement of the blinds and a gentle clattering as they sway in the warm breeze. I'm sure I closed the windows before I left the house. In fact, I'm certain. I walk slowly into the room, hardly daring to breathe. I feel like a burglar in my own home. The bed looks exactly as it did after I made it this morning. I lean over and examine the pillows for any signs, a stray long hair, for example, but there's nothing. I go over and shut the window. Maybe I *didn't* close them before I left. I look again at Simon's reply. *Anything wrong?* Is he panicking now, sweating because he's worried he left the window open? Did he open it because I might smell her perfume in here? Because the room might smell of sex? Oh God, stop it. I sit down heavily on the bed. The more I think like this, the worse it gets. He said he'd be back by six thirty, but of course he isn't, and just after I've got Bonnie to bed, he messages to say he's been held up talking to a parent and it'll be about half past seven by the time he gets in.

We're having mushroom risotto tonight – Anna showed me how to make it – and as I stir the risotto rice into the butter and olive oil, I'm still trying to think of some reasonable explanation. It crosses my mind that Anna knows where the spare key is because she uses it when she looks after Bonnie. But on the other hand, why on earth would she want to let herself into our house when I'm not here, make a cup of tea, and then go again? It makes no sense. It keeps nagging at me, though, and I suppose it's possible that she was out and about, maybe needed the loo or didn't feel well or something ... I pick up my phone and type: *This is going to sound really weird, and I'll explain when I see you, but I don't suppose you popped into the house today while I was out, did you? Maybe to use the loo or something? Honestly not a problem, just wanted to check. Can you let me know? Thanks! Xxx* and I add a smiling emoji.

She replies a few minutes later. *No! Wouldn't dream of letting myself in while you're not there. Certainly not without asking you first. Everything ok?*

Then I feel shit for even thinking it. I'm pleased that she's asked if everything's okay, though, because she seemed a bit frosty this morning. Or maybe it's my imagination. *Sorry, didn't think you would – just needed to check. Yes, all fine, thanks. See you tomorrow xxx*

I hear Simon coming in as I'm sloshing some wine into the risotto, and I pour us both a glass to have with supper. As we're eating, I try to sound as casual as possible as I say, 'By the way, what did you pop home for today? Did you forget something?'

He looks up, his face a mix of curiosity and surprise. 'What are you talking about?'

'Well, when I got back this afternoon, you'd obviously been here, but you'd gone again by then, so I was wondering—'

'What do you mean, I'd "obviously" been here? Of course I didn't pop home. I never pop home – it's a half-hour drive, for God's sake!'

Carefully, I top up his glass and then my own. 'How come the kettle was still warm when I got back, then?'

He gives me an odd look. 'I'm guessing you boiled it just before you went out. What does it matter?'

'Simon, I was out for nearly seven hours. No kettle stays warm for that long.'

'Well, I don't bloody know. Why do you—'

'And the bedroom window was open, but I closed it before I left.'

He throws his fork down onto the plate. 'Maybe the kettle switched itself on. Maybe the window opened itself. How should I know? What the fuck are you getting at, Emily?'

I find myself swallowing. *Stay calm*, I tell myself. 'I think you're lying to me,' I say, and something flashes across his face. Guilt? I'd intended to confront him properly, to tell him I *knew* he'd brought Sarah back here while I was out, but there's a tiny voice in the back of my head telling me I might be wrong, that there might be another explanation.

He stands up, pushing his chair back roughly so that it scrapes against the floor. 'This is ridiculous, Emily, and you've got to stop, all right?' He's trying not to shout, I can tell. 'Why would I creep back here during the day and then lie to you about it? You probably put the kettle on automatically when you came in without realising it. As for the open window, you're always forgetting to close windows when you go out.'

'But I know I—'

Simon bangs his fist down on the table. 'Stop it, Em. This paranoia of yours is going to get you in trouble one of these days.'

With that, he picks up his phone and keys, and leaving half a plate of risotto – the first meal I've cooked from scratch in ages, he says, 'I'm going out. I'll be back in a couple of hours. Oh, and in case you're wondering, I'm not seeing another woman, all right?' He slams the door.

CHAPTER EIGHTEEN

It's Friday today, so I didn't set my alarm last night and it's gone seven when I wake up. When I go downstairs, Simon's already in the kitchen, encouraging Bonnie to eat the last of her Marmite soldiers. 'Ah, you're up.' He drains his coffee cup and gets to his feet. 'Right, I'd better go. See you tonight.' He's barely spoken to me since that row we had on Monday night when he stormed out in the middle of supper. It's the angriest I've seen him since we've been together. He kisses Bonnie on the head and picks up his phone and keys. He's wearing the white linen shirt again, the one that really shows off his deepening tan. As he kisses me – at least he's kissing me goodbye again, but it's a chaste kiss that barely brushes my lips – his cheek touches mine and I feel the smoothness of his skin and smell the intoxicating combination of aftershave and shower gel. I know I'm lucky to be married to this gorgeous, sexy man, but I wish I could stop being so suspicious. Just because he left Sarah for me doesn't mean he's going to leave me to go back to Sarah.

'By the way,' he says as he turns to go, 'don't worry about supper for me tonight. I'll grab something for myself when I get in.'

'What? Why? I was going to—'

But he cuts me off. 'I'm going for a few pints with Marcus.' Then he sort of lifts his chin as he looks at me, as if he's challenging me to object.

'But it's Friday night!' He knows Friday night is date night. 'I got us one of those "dine in" deals from M&S,' I say. 'Couple of steaks, salad, some buttered new potatoes. And crème brûlées for after.'

'Sounds good,' he says. 'But it'll keep until tomorrow, won't it?'

'I suppose so, but . . .'

'Great. See you later,' he says, and then he's gone.

I try to shake off the feeling of sadness as I eat my breakfast. It's a lovely, sunny day again, but I'm stuck inside until the boiler guy comes, which could be anytime between now and 4pm. Just as well, I suppose, because I've got loads of emails to catch up on, and lessons to plan for Years 8 and 9. I don't mind a few hours' work on Fridays because there's usually a nice evening to look forward to. Simon never goes out on Friday night, especially not at the last minute. For once, I don't automatically assume he's seeing Sarah, because I'm pretty sure he's doing this to punish me for accusing him of lying. Although I suppose if he *was* seeing Sarah, being annoyed with me would be a good cover . . . *Oh Christ, I'm doing it again.*

'Come on, Bon-bons.' I stand up so that I can lift Bonnie out of her highchair. 'Let's get you dressed.' I've just unstrapped her when Oscar jumps onto the table. I reach out to stroke him and he arches his back against my hand. 'Tat!' Bonnie says, pointing.

'Yes, cat – clever girl! Do you want to help me give him his breakfast?'

'Deh.' She nods.

Glad of the distraction, I lift her from her highchair and set her down on the floor before taking her hand so she can lead me into the utility room, Oscar meowing and weaving around our legs. 'Right, can you get Oscar's bowl for me?'

Bonnie picks up Oscar's dish and hands it to me with an air of importance. 'Okay, now we need some cat food. Can you get one of his pouches out of the cupboard?'

She nods, toddles over to the cupboard where I keep the food, opens the door and squats in front of it with her hands on her knees. Usually, she reaches in and picks up a pouch straightaway, but when she's still peering into the cupboard after a few moments, I remember taking the last one in the box. 'Hang on, sweetie. Let Mummy open a new box then you can choose his breakfast.'

I reach in to pull out a pack of salmon and sardine dinners, and that's when I see my hoop earrings, sitting on the shelf, next to the box of cat food. I stand there for a second, looking at them, racking my brains. I have absolutely no recollection of putting them there. I vaguely remember wearing them a week or so ago, but if I'd taken them off down here, I'd have left them on the kitchen top. Why on earth would I have put my earrings in the bloody cat food cupboard? And if I did, why can't I remember doing it? It would be funny if it weren't so unsettling. I find myself thinking about a book I read a few years ago, about a woman who developed a rare, hereditary form of dementia at the age of thirty-six. It flashes through my mind again that there could be something like that in my family history and I wouldn't know anything about it. But no, I don't forget things that often, and I'm a hundred – well, ninety-nine – per cent certain I didn't put those earrings there.

CHAPTER NINETEEN

I can't face staying late at school tonight so I pack up my stuff just after four and head out to the car. It's ridiculously hot, even for June. I barely slept last night, partly because of the heat, but also because things are still tense between Simon and me. It wasn't too bad over the weekend, and we had the steaks on Saturday night but it was hardly what you'd call a romantic evening. It doesn't help that he asked me last night if I thought that alcohol was making me paranoid. It's not as if I drink *that* much – well, not regularly, anyway. It's not unknown for me to overdo it, but then everyone does now and again, don't they? And to be honest, what working mum doesn't look forward to a glass or two of wine at the end of a long day? Anyway, in an attempt to patch things up, I rashly agreed to have a couple of nights a week off, but now as I'm walking to the car, I realise I'm already thinking about having a glass of wine when I get in. It's another thing about this weather – blazing sunshine makes me want a beautifully chilled, crisp, dry white, condensation misting the glass. I bet he'll still have a beer as soon as he gets in. I sigh as I click my seatbelt into place and turn on the ignition.

Anna's just getting Bonnie out of her car as I arrive. They've been stuck in traffic, Anna explains, as I reach out to take a very sweaty-looking Bonnie from her arms.

'She must be boiling, bless her,' Anna says. 'The traffic lights were out at that big crossroads as you come down the hill from Gemma's. It was absolute chaos.'

As soon as we're inside, I open the windows in a futile attempt to let some air in, while Anna strips Bonnie down to her nappy. Then she wets a cloth under the tap, wrings it out and gently wipes Bonnie's overheated face. 'There, that's better, isn't it, chicken?' she says, and Bonnie nods gratefully. Why didn't I think to make my daughter more comfortable before doing anything else? Next, Anna settles Bonnie in her highchair and puts a plate of sliced watermelon in front of her. 'There you go, my darling.' She drops a kiss on Bonnie's head and then turns to me. 'You're home early,' she says.

'Yeah, couldn't face staying there any longer in this heat.' I watch Bonnie happily cramming watermelon into her mouth as the pink juice runs down her arms and chest. I kiss her sticky face. 'Is that nice?'

She nods. 'Mmm.'

'Glass of wine?' Anna moves towards the fridge. 'You look like you need it.'

'No, thanks, not today. I told Simon I was going to try and cut down.'

Anna's face darkens. 'What's it got to do with him?' There's a hard edge to her voice, which she clearly notices herself because her eyelids sort of flutter as though she's embarrassed. 'Sorry, I mean, it's nothing to do with me, but ... but I've got to say it, why are you letting Simon tell you what to do? If you want a glass of wine, have a glass of wine.'

At which point I surprise myself by bursting into tears. I half expect Anna to put her arms around me, but she sort of hovers, and then I see Bonnie's lower lip wobble and I pull myself together quickly. 'Sorry.' I reach for the kitchen roll to blow my nose. 'It's been a rough day and I didn't sleep well last night.' I smile at Bonnie. 'Mummy's fine, sweetheart,' I say. 'Just being silly.' I force another big grin until, apparently satisfied, she turns her attention back to her watermelon.

Anna pours us both a glass of wine, a tiny one for herself as usual, and I tell her about the tension between Simon and me, the horrible row we had last week, and what he said about alcohol making me paranoid.

'Was that what the row was about?'

'No.' I hesitate. If I tell her, will she think I'm paranoid, too? But I decide to risk it, and so I explain about being out all day on Monday, and coming home to find the window open and the kettle still warm, and how the only explanation I could think of was that Simon had been home and then gone back to school.

'Ah,' she says, 'so that's why you wondered if I'd let myself in! But why do you think he'd come home and then make out he didn't?'

Again, I hesitate, but I'm suddenly overwhelmed by the need to talk about it. So I tell her my suspicions, about the many late meetings, the way he and Sarah look when they're talking to each other. 'The other thing . . . I know it sounds silly, but remember I was telling you the other day about how he was engaged to her when he met me? Well, part of me thinks it could be karma, you know? That if he went back to her – or if he met someone else while he was married to me – it would serve me right.'

She doesn't immediately tell me not to be so silly. Instead, her brow furrows even more deeply. Eventually, she says, 'I'm sure there's another explanation.' But she doesn't sound that sure at all.

'He said I probably forgot to shut the window, and that maybe I'd switched the kettle on without thinking as soon as I got in. But if I'd done that, it would have been hot, and it wasn't. It was warm, like it had been boiled an hour or so ago.'

'Hmm, I see what you mean.'

'What do you think, then? Tell me honestly. Do you think I'm being paranoid?'

A moment passes before she says anything – she looks as if she's forming her answer carefully. 'I don't want to say anything against Simon, because I don't really know him, but . . .'

'Go on. But?'

'But I sometimes think when he comes home from work that he seems to have made a lot of effort with how he looks.'

I'm about to say he's not really making any special effort

because he always looks good, when she continues. 'I suppose if he *was* cheating on you, that would explain why he's trying to make out it's you being paranoid.'

It's getting on for eight when Simon finally arrives home. I didn't notice this morning, but he's wearing a blue-and-white print shirt today, the top two buttons undone and sunglasses tucked into the top. Even though it's a scorching hot day, he still manages to look cool and sexy. Perhaps he *is* making more effort than usual.

'I've only just got Bonnie off to sleep,' I say, 'so I'm going to nip up and have a shower before we eat. I thought we'd have a chicken and avocado salad tonight — it's too hot to cook.'

'Sounds good,' he says. 'Shall we eat outside? I'll lay the table.'

In the bedroom, I strip off my work clothes and am about to step into the shower when I notice the bed isn't how I left it this morning. I always pull the duvet up over the first pillow, then I put the second pillow on top, angled against the headboard. But the pillows are both on top of the duvet, and they're not angled right. I stand there, naked in the middle of the room, staring at the bed. Am I being paranoid? Could I have been in a hurry this morning and not made the bed properly? But I didn't have a drink last night, I wasn't foggy or disorientated when I got up, and I know I made the bed in exactly the same way I always do. Which can only mean the bed has been . . . used.

CHAPTER TWENTY

Simon says goodbye to Bonnie, then comes over to kiss me. I'm watching the coffee machine and I don't turn, so he drops a kiss on my cheek. 'Are you all right?' he says, hovering by the door with his keys in his hand. 'Only you're acting as if I've done something wrong.'

'No, I'm fine.' I try a half-smile as I turn towards him, but I can't meet his eye. It's been torturing me since yesterday, ever since I noticed the bed looking different to how I *know* I left it. But if I say anything, he'll say I'm being paranoid like he did a couple of weeks ago when I came home to find the kettle warm and the bedroom window open. What reasonable explanation could there be anyway?

He hovers a bit longer, then says, 'Okay, if you're sure. I'll see you tonight, then. Probably about half seven – there's a meeting at five thirty, and then I said I'd play a quick game of squash with Marcus, okay?'

'Isn't it a bit hot for squash?'

'We'll probably only have one game. It makes you appreciate the nice cold shower afterwards.'

'Oh, right. See you later then.'

It's only as I'm driving to school that I realise he wasn't carrying his squash bag.

School is oddly quiet now GCSEs are over and Year 11s have left. It's only one year group missing, and yet they leave a gap that makes it seem more than that. My timetable's lighter, which should be a good thing, but it means I have more time to think, and my thoughts keep returning to Simon and Sarah. I'm so distracted that at one point, even one of the kids asks me if I'm all right. I hate feeling like this, but what am I supposed to think? At lunchtime, I manage about three mouthfuls of my sandwich but I can barely swallow, so I end up chucking the rest of it in the bin and going for a walk instead. While I'm walking, I have an idea, and I text Anna. *Is your car working okay at the moment? And if so – I know this is an odd request – could I borrow it for a couple of hours this evening? I'll explain later.*

No probs, she replies. *Sounds interesting.*

When I get back to school, I go looking for one of the other assistant heads. There's no sign of Rob or Bev in the staffroom, but I find Bev at one of the computers in the Humanities office, so I sit down at the monitor next to her and log in to the school intranet.

'Oh, by the way,' I say casually, 'I forgot to ask Simon what time he'd be back tonight – do you happen to know if there's a meeting this afternoon?'

'Yeah, heads of year meeting. Upper school. Should only be about an hour, though.' She doesn't take her eyes off the screen. 'And it bloody better not be much more than that. My husband's starting to forget what I look like.'

I smile. 'I'm starting to feel that way about Simon. Thanks Bev.'

With fewer lessons to teach, I'm home by four, so I have some time to play with Bonnie before I set off back to school in Anna's car.

'He'd spot my car straightaway,' I explain to Anna. 'There's definitely a meeting, because I've checked, but I want to see what time he comes out of school, and whether he's with her. Sarah.'

'Good luck,' Anna says, handing me the keys. 'Don't get caught!'

As I take the keys from her, I get the slightest whiff of cigarette smoke, like I did once before. 'I can smell cigarettes,' I say. 'You don't smoke, do you, Anna?' I try to make it sound light, as though I'm being ironic.

She shakes her head as she turns back to the fish fingers she's grilling for Bonnie's tea. 'Not since I was about fifteen,' she says. 'Must be someone outside. That's the only trouble with having all the windows and doors open, you have to put up with everybody else's smells and noises.'

This is true. But the only smells we usually get around here are barbecues. Then I remember finding those cigarette ends in the alley that time. I haven't found any since then, but on the other hand, I haven't really looked, because it's a few weeks since I had that feeling of being watched, so maybe whoever it was has moved on. Or maybe Simon was right all along, and it was just someone who didn't want their parents or partner to know they smoked.

I pull into the school car park just after six in case the meeting finishes early. I doubt Simon would recognise Anna's Skoda even if he saw it, but just in case, I park right over in the corner where, thankfully, there's a patch of shade. It's still hot, though, and Anna's car doesn't have air con, so I fan myself with my book and kick myself for not bringing a bottle of water. It's so hot in the car, I'm tempted to get out for a few moments but I don't want to risk missing him, so I sit there sweating as I watch, waiting for him to appear. It's almost seven when Bev hurries out of the building and down the steps. As she pulls away with a slight screech of tyres, I spot them. Simon and Sarah, walking together. I slide down in my seat, heart hammering. Am I going to follow them? Then Simon gets into his car, and Sarah crosses the tarmac and gets into hers. She drives away first, but Simon isn't far behind. I wonder if he's following her to her flat, or whether they're going to meet somewhere?

I start the engine and pull out after them. I've lost sight of Sarah now, but there's only a van between me and Simon, so I follow him steadily for a couple of miles until he turns into the car park of The Plough. I manage to find a space on the other side of the road, and I watch as he gets out and strolls into the pub. There's no sign of Sarah's car, at least not yet.

I want to feel relieved, but I can't relax yet because he told me he was playing squash, and now here he is in the pub. I don't know where Sarah lives, so maybe she's driven home and will arrive on foot any minute. I glance at the clock. It's just gone seven. Anna said she'll stay until eight if necessary. If he's meeting Sarah, surely she'll be here soon. I huddle down in the seat again and wait. A few minutes later, a blue BMW that I recognise swings into the car park and Marcus hurries into the bar.

After sitting there for another twenty minutes, I close my eyes and put my head down on the steering wheel. It looks like it's just Simon and Marcus, having a drink. I don't know what to think anymore. Sometimes I wonder if I really am going crazy. I'm about to head home when my phone pings a message. Simon. *You were right — too hot for squash! Went for a drink with Marcus instead. Leaving the pub now — should be back before eight so can say goodnight to Bon if she's still awake.*

Shit! I've just started the engine when I see him coming out of the pub, still holding his phone. I pull out onto the main road and put my foot down, only to get caught by the first set of lights. 'Come on, come on,' I mutter, eyes darting back and forth to the rear-view mirror as I wait for the lights to change. I shoot over the next set just as they're turning red, and after that it's a straight run home. It's only minutes after I let myself into the house that I hear Simon's key in the door. Thank God for Anna, who has got Bonnie ready for bed, made pesto and boiled some pasta for supper. 'Thank you so much,' I say, pulling Bonnie onto my lap with her book so it looks like we've been there for a while. I'm hot and sweaty from rushing, and my fringe is sticking to my forehead.

'Hey,' Simon says as he comes into the kitchen. 'Did you get my message?'

'Yes – sorry, meant to reply. I knew you wouldn't be playing squash, anyway. You forgot your kit.'

'No, I didn't.' He smiles. 'It's in the car. We were going to play last week, remember? It's still there from then.'

'Ah. Okay.'

He puts his arms out to Bonnie. 'Come and give Daddy a cuddle.'

'Do you want to take her up? Supper's ready whenever you want it.'

'All right then,' he says. 'Come on, Missus Madam,' he lifts her off my lap, 'up to bye-byes.' And after Bonnie says her goodnights, off they go up the stairs, Simon chattering away to Bonnie and Bonnie making happy noises back.

Anna and I look at each other. 'Phew,' I say. 'That was close.'

'Well? Anything to report?'

'No, thank goodness. He was telling the truth, this time at least.' I consider telling her about the bed, but that's not going to be a five-minute conversation and anyway, it feels too sordid to talk about.

'Right, then,' Anna says. 'I'd better get going.'

'Thanks again, Anna. For letting me borrow your car, and for sorting out Bonnie and supper and everything.'

She smiles her wide smile. 'No problem at all,' she

says. 'Oh, by the way – did you say you'd be able to bring some chicken drumsticks tomorrow? I've made some coleslaw and—'

'Oh shit! I'm so sorry, Anna, I completely forgot to mention – I'm going to have to rearrange tomorrow.' I explain about Zoe's email having gone astray, and that she's going away for a year so tomorrow's the only possible day. 'I'm really sorry to mess you about. I meant to tell you straight away, but I've been so preoccupied with Simon, it went out of my head. And Zoe's one of my oldest friends. Can we make it next week instead?' I realise it seems as though I'm putting Zoe before Anna in the friend stakes, when in fact Anna's been a better friend than Zoe these last couple of months.

'Next week?' Anna says; there's that hard edge in her voice again. 'What about all the food?'

'Oh, yes, of course – sorry. Maybe Saturday, then.'

'Saturday? I suppose so. I don't think I've got anything else on during the day.'

'Okay, let's make it Saturday.'

'I'll let you know for sure when I've checked my diary,' she says. The way she says it makes it clear she doesn't like me assuming she'll be free.

'Yes, I meant if you're not busy, obviously.'

Then she says, 'Do you want me to look after Bonnie while you meet your friend?'

'Oh, no, it's fine. I asked Gemma to have her for a few hours, then Simon's going to pick her up later. He's free most of the afternoon tomorrow.' What I don't say is, at least if he's looking after Bonnie, he can't be seeing Sarah. But then it occurs to me that there's no reason at all that he couldn't see Sarah at the same time, because Bonnie can't tell me what he's been up to, can she?

'I could easily have had her, you know, if you'd asked.'

'What? Oh, sorry, I mean ... thank you. I know you'd have had her like a shot, but I didn't ask because with you working at the pub in the evening as well, I thought you might—'

'I like looking after her. I've said.' She doesn't look at me as she gathers her keys, sunglasses and the paperback she's reading and stuffs them into her bag. She's pissed off. 'I'm sorry, Anna. I should have thought and asked you first. I didn't want to put any extra pressure on you, that's all.'

She nods, barely glancing at me as she leaves. I'm not sure what she's more upset about – that I didn't ask her to look after Bonnie or that I've put off our plans for tomorrow. Either way, I feel guilty. I've taken her for granted and I've let her down.

Simon and I are sitting out on the terrace with a glass of wine after supper. I watch him closely, but he seems normal and relaxed, and as we sit here, I wonder again whether I'm imagining things, whether there's a simple explanation for all of it.

I love sitting outside in the evenings, although the garden's looking a bit parched. I keep forgetting to water the grass and it's drying out so much in this heat, it's starting to go brown.

It's lovely, having a good-sized garden, but neither of us is a keen gardener so we don't really do much with it. Maybe I'll have a go at tackling it over the summer break.

Everyone's outside tonight, enjoying the balmy summer evening. I can hear the neighbours chatting, the occasional clink of glasses, and the odd pop of a cork and bubble of gentle laughter. I think about how nice it is to be out here at this time, watching the sun go down behind the trees. It's still hot, but not unbearably so. I try to push my worries about Simon to the back of my mind and concentrate on the here and now – Bonnie sleeping peacefully in her cot; my handsome, successful husband who just had a quick drink with his friend before coming home to me; the gentle hum of conversation from the other gardens; and Oscar, my furry companion, curled up on the sun lounger where he's been all evening. It's nearly ten o'clock and it's only just starting to get dark. The conversations around us gradually die down as our neighbours begin to call it a night and go into their houses, throwing their empty bottles into the recycling bins as they go.

After a while, Simon stretches and looks at his phone. 'Half ten,' he says. 'I'd better get to bed.' He grins at me. 'Some of us have to go to work in the morning, you know.'

I roll my eyes. I can't believe he still thinks I'm amused by that, but I let it go. 'Okay,' I say. 'I won't be long, but I think I'll just sit here for a while. It's so lovely and peaceful out here.'

'It is, isn't it?' he says, hands in his pockets as he stands on the terrace, looking out at the warm, still garden. 'Right,' he says, kissing me on the forehead. 'Don't forget the windows when you lock up.'

'I won't.' For a second, I'm tempted to grab his hand and kiss it because I'm feeling guilty now for following him and watching him like that. Is this what I've come to? Stalking my own husband? But then I remember how the bed looked yesterday. I know for certain that's not how I left it.

I pour the last of the wine into my glass and as I look out over the darkening garden, I start to feel slightly unnerved. It's as though a chill has settled over the night, even though the air is still warm. I look down towards the end of the garden, but it's completely dark now, so I can only see as far as the outside light reaches, which is about halfway down the lawn. As I look beyond that point, down to the far end where the shrubs and trees are just shadowy black shapes against a navy-blue sky, I'm aware of a horrible, prickling sensation. It's the same feeling I had back in the spring when I was getting all those funny phone calls. And in those first few weeks after Bonnie was born – the feeling that there's someone or something out there, watching the house.

I try to ignore the feeling as I go back inside for another drink. I fancy a gin and tonic, and I make it with ice, lime and a couple of slices of cucumber so it feels a bit more special. When I go back outside, Oscar's no longer on the sun lounger. He's probably off on a late-night hunting expedition. I can't hear anyone else talking now, and the only sound is the clinking of the ice in my glass. As I reflect on the perfect combination of the cold, sharp bitterness of the tonic and fiery warmth of the gin, I shiver slightly. Maybe it's the ice. I'm hoping the gin will drown out this creepy feeling, but it doesn't.

It's getting late now anyway, and I've slept so badly the last few nights, the tiredness is beginning to catch up with me. I finish my drink, draining the last drops of gin through the ice, then get to my feet. 'Oscar,' I call, but not loudly enough to disturb the neighbours. 'Come on, puss, bedtime.' I listen for the sound of him rustling through the shrubbery. 'Oscar,' I call again in a stage whisper. Silence. I try once more, but he's obviously having more fun out there in the undergrowth, so he'll have to come in through the cat flap later. I go back inside and lock the French doors. This weather must be a burglar's paradise, and with that alley running between the gardens at the back, we're vulnerable here. As I pull the curtains firmly across to shut out the darkness, I'm overtaken by another involuntary shiver, even though it's not remotely chilly.

CHAPTER TWENTY-ONE

On my way to meet Zoe, I message Simon just to make sure he hasn't forgotten he's picking Bonnie up from Gemma's at one. He replies immediately: *getting in the car now*.

Great. I type back, and I ask him to keep an eye out for Oscar, who I haven't seen since last night.

Zoe and I meet in the pizza place overlooking the Thames. We have a table near the window where we can watch the sun glancing off the water in dancing silver streaks. We spend the first ten minutes chatting about our families, and I'm touched that she asks about Bonnie and doesn't appear bored by the answers. We order our pizzas, with olives and bread to start and a bottle of Shiraz.

'I'll have to go easy, though.' She smiles. 'I can't drink at lunchtime anymore.'

I have a sudden memory of getting horribly pissed that day I took Anna out to lunch when we first got to know each other. That was embarrassing. But there's something about being with people, especially people I want to like me, that makes me drink too much, too quickly. I decide to take it easy today. It's been so long since Zoe and I have been out together, I really don't want to spoil it.

The wine, bread and olives arrive quickly and we're soon chatting almost as easily as we used to. We talk about work for a bit, how she hates her new job and has handed her notice in after six months. 'It's well paid,' she says, 'but I'm sick of the stress. I'm not sure what I want to do next, really, which is why I took this job in Greece. We'll do that for a year, then take stock, see how we feel.'

'We?'

'Oh, that's right – I haven't told you yet, have I?' She smiles as she dips a chunk of bread in olive oil. 'I've been seeing someone. His name's Dom – Dominic. You may have seen on Facebook.'

'I'm hardly ever on there these days, but I did see a photo of you and a seriously hot, dark-haired guy in a cocktail bar.'

'That's Dom. He's sick of his job too, so we're going to work in the sun for a few months, then decide what to do next.'

'Well,' I say. 'Good for you.'

We chat a bit more, and I tell her about my return to Woodview as a subject teacher and how I feel like I've taken a big step back. 'But there are plusses, too. I get to spend more time with Bonnie, which was the whole point, but also, having been off for a year, a lot of the people who weren't speaking to me have left now, and those who haven't seem to have at least partly forgiven me.'

Zoe nods. 'That's good. Bit unfair to blame you entirely. Speaking of which, your email.'

'Yes?' I say.

'I definitely replied.' She shows me her screen. 'See?'

'It's okay – I believe you.' But I still glance at the email in her 'sent' folder, dated 2 May – my mum's birthday. It's quite brief, but she apologises for not having been in touch, so that's something.

'Anyway,' she says, 'you're right, things do seem to have changed a bit, but it's not about what happened when you met Simon. Not entirely, anyway.'

Not entirely. 'Go on.'

'What I mean is, I wasn't keen on you marrying someone who dumped his previous fiancé so easily. You know what they say, *when a man marries his mistress, it creates a vacancy.*' She looks at me. 'Sorry – I shouldn't have said that. Who knows, maybe I'd have done the same thing in your shoes.'

I nod. 'Okay. But you said it's not really about that?'

She's taking an unusually long time to spear an olive. Then she sighs. 'Christ, this is difficult.'

'Come on, Zo, what is it? We're supposed to be friends, so if I've done something to upset you, I need to know. I need you to tell me the truth.'

'All right. You've asked, so I'm going to tell you. It's just . . . I'm uncomfortable about what happened the last time you, me and Tash went out.'

'What do you mean? I can't even remember the last time we had a night out. What happened?'

'You don't remember?'

'Sorry, no. I don't even know when you're talking about. We've had a lot of nights out, the three of us.'

'Yes, but not for ages.'

'Huh,' I say, 'that's true enough. You just disappeared after I married Simon, both of you.'

'But—'

'All right, you popped round a couple of times after I had Bonnie, but it was obvious I'd done something to annoy you. And I don't think I've seen Tash since I got married.'

She takes a sip of her wine. 'No, you probably won't have seen Tash.' She's looking at me now. 'Do you really not remember the last time we went out? It would have been the last time you saw Tash, I imagine.'

I shrug, moving my hand onto my lap so that she doesn't see my fingers tapping the table in irritation. 'I don't know. Where did we go?'

'We started off at the wine bar in Blackheath. We had a nice meal, couple of bottles of wine between the three of us, it was fine. But you didn't want to go home, so we had another bottle, and when we got kicked out of there, we ended up going on to that club, Lacey's. Do you remember?'

'Vaguely. We went there a few times, didn't we?'

'Yes, but the last time you got absolutely rat-arsed.'

'Did I? I don't remember.'

'I'm not surprised,' she mutters, and before I can say anything else, our pizzas arrive, so we wait until the waitress has gone.

'So, I got drunk on a night out with my mates.' I force a laugh. 'In fact, I think I do vaguely remember being in that wine bar. Was that the night we sat in the upstairs bit and there was that really annoying bloke behind the bar who kept trying to chat you up?'

'Yes! That was it. Kept calling us "girls". Tash kept sneezing because her hay fever was bad. You were upset when you arrived because you'd had another row with your mum. Or maybe not a row, but you'd definitely seen her that day and you were upset.'

'Ha! Not unusual. But yes, it's beginning to come back to me now. I don't recall the club, though. What did I do, fall over on the dance floor or something?'

'Come on, you must remember, surely?'

'No, I don't.' I'm starting to feel both annoyed and uncomfortable. Zoe looks serious. 'Come on, just tell me, Zoe, please. What happened?'

'Oh God, this is awkward.' She puts her knife and fork down and pauses for a moment as if she's trying to find the right words. 'You *did* fall over on the dance floor, but it wasn't only that. It was the way you were with Billy.'

'Billy? Who's Billy?'

'Tash's boyfriend at the time. He joined us at the club, and you were all over him. I don't mean just flirting, I mean literally, draping your arms around his neck, dancing *really* close. You couldn't keep your hands off him. You tried to snog him more than once, and at one point, he was holding your arms by your sides to stop you. But then a bit later,

Tash went to the loo, and when she came back, she saw you snogging him at the bar.' She stops. 'God, you really don't have any recollection at all, do you?'

I'm still holding my knife and fork but I can't move. Slowly, I put the cutlery down and take a mouthful of wine. I use my serviette to wipe the tear that's slipping down my face as I lower my head and rest it in my hand. 'I . . . I don't know what to say,' I mutter. 'I don't . . . I can't . . .'

Zoe leans across the table and touches my arm. 'You were pissed,' she says, more gently now. I think she actually feels sorry for me. 'It was obvious. But the thing was, you'd just told us about Simon, and that he'd been engaged to that other girl. So it seemed a bit . . .' She shrugs. 'I don't know, I suppose putting it crudely, it looked like you didn't care whose boyfriend you were after.'

'Christ,' I whisper. 'No wonder I've not heard from her.' I can't meet Zoe's eye. I try to say more but there's such a huge lump forming in my throat, it seems impossible.

'I'm sorry, Em. I should have said something before. I didn't realise you were that bothered about not seeing us. You seemed so wrapped up in Simon. And that night in the club, I thought you were just being a bit reckless because you were about to get married. I don't think either of us thought you were really trying to get off with Billy, but Tash was upset that you didn't apologise after.'

I'm shaking my head. 'But I—'

Zoe continues. 'I didn't realise you'd forgotten all this.'

'Honestly, I have absolutely no recollection of any of it.' I take a big gulp of wine and I realise my hand is trembling. 'So, what happened? Did it cause trouble between Tash and . . . ?'

'Billy.' Zoe shrugs. 'Yeah, a bit, but they got over it.' She takes another mouthful of wine. 'It was obvious you were drunk.'

I feel myself flinch at the stark, brutal truth of that statement. Shame makes me bow my head. My hands are in my lap, and I realise I've been tearing the serviette to pieces.

'They ended up moving in together,' she continues. 'But they broke up about six months later. She caught him cheating on her. He even brought the girl back to their flat while she was at work. Can you believe that?'

'Seriously? What a shit.'

'Yeah.' Zoe takes a sip of wine. 'He seemed so nice at first. Very charming. But Tash knew he was up to something, she just needed proof.' Zoe looks at me. 'Don't you even recall meeting him that night?'

I shake my head. 'No, I remember us being in the wine bar, and I remember us all laughing about that bloke who fancied you, but that's it. I have no memory of the club. I don't even remember leaving the wine bar.' Slowly, I pick up my glass and take a sip. 'I'm mortified to think I behaved like that. I'll email Tash and apologise. I know it's a bit late, but I suppose better late than never.'

Zoe nods. 'Can't do any harm. I've not seen Tash for a bit myself – been too busy with work. But I'm sure she'll be pleased to hear from you.'

After the waitress has cleared our plates, Zoe says, 'Anyway, how's it all been with your mum? Have you tried talking to her again?'

'No.' I shake my head. 'Not recently. I will do soon, though. She won't like it. As far as she's concerned, my life started the day they brought me home and I shouldn't be interested in anything that happened before. I don't think she knows much about my birth parents – I don't think she wanted to know.'

'You know you're entitled to see your adoption file, don't you?'

I nod. 'I don't feel I can, though. Not yet, anyway. I don't want to do it behind her back, but I don't feel I can tell her. All I want is for her to agree that it's important for me to know whatever there is to know.'

Zoe sighs. 'But she's not going to, is she? I mean, this has been bothering you ever since I've known you. How many times have you brought it up and she's changed the subject? She's not going to suddenly change her mind, is she?'

'Probably not, but maybe I've not pushed it far enough in the past. It's become a much bigger issue since I got pregnant. Having a baby makes you think more about who you are, whose genes you're passing down. And one day, Bonnie'll want to know about her roots, too. Maybe not until she has a baby herself, but she'll want to know at some point. I've tried discussing that with my mum, but she doesn't even want me to tell Bonnie I'm adopted.'

I can hear her voice now. *Why not let the poor child believe*

I'm her grandma? I don't know why you have to complicate everything . . .

Zoe shakes her head. 'I suppose it's the idea that what you don't know can't hurt you.'

'Except it can,' we say in unison, then we smile.

'Anyway,' Zoe says, 'how's everything else?'

In the old days I'd have poured out all my worries about Simon and Sarah – the looks between them, the late nights at school, that feeling that she's been in my house, in my bed. I'm not sure why I don't say anything. Maybe I'm afraid Zoe'll say something to make me even more sure I can't trust him. 'Oh, everything else is okay, really. The bloody cat's gone missing again, but apart from that . . .' I shrug. 'Anyway, tell me more about Tash and this Billy guy? How did she find out he was cheating on her?'

'Actually, that's quite a story. You'll never guess what she did!'

CHAPTER TWENTY-TWO

I wouldn't say Zoe and I are back to normal, but we're getting there, and when she hugged me goodbye, it felt warm and genuine. As I walk home after our lunch, I mentally compose an apologetic email to Tash. I think back to what Zoe told me – how Tash had suspected her boyfriend was cheating on her, even though there weren't any real tell-tale signs. It was a gut feeling, she said. So I ended up telling her about Simon and Sarah after all. She was sympathetic, of course, but I got the feeling there might have been a *told you so* lurking unsaid in the background. And then she told me how Tash had found a way to get proof. It sounds so simple and easy, and yet so dramatic. I could do the same thing, and then I'd know for sure. My stomach somersaults at the thought.

I'm not sure why I check, because I'm certain I didn't get Zoe's email, but as I make my way home, I take out my phone and scroll through the deleted folder, and there it is.

I must have deleted it by accident without even reading it. That's weird. I remember that day because it was my mum's birthday, the day I lost my phone and Anna brought it round. Maybe that's how I ended up deleting it – checking my emails and chatting with Anna at the same time. Oh well. At least Zoe replied.

When I get back, Simon and Bonnie are sitting in the shade at the end of the garden, Simon working on his laptop, Bonnie playing with her Duplo blocks. It looks like Oscar hasn't been back. I don't leave food down overnight, so I can't tell whether he came in last night or not, but the food I put down this morning hasn't been touched and there are flies buzzing around it so I pick it up and scrape it into the bin. I hope this doesn't mean he's gone walkabout again. He was missing for almost a week last time. It's odd because he's not a cat that wanders very often; it just seems that when he does, he does it big time. We leave the doors open all evening, but there's still no sign of him by the time we're ready for bed. I stand outside for a few minutes, calling and shaking his biscuit box, but still nothing.

I find him in the morning, staggering around outside the back door. He looks as if he's been trying to come in through the cat flap, but he's disorientated and keeps butting the side of the flap with his nose. When I pick him up, I can feel him trembling, then his legs seem to go into spasm. 'There's something wrong with him,' I shout through to Simon. 'We need to get him to the vet. Can you call them, tell them we're on the way?'

Oscar's still twitching and trembling when I put him into the cat carrier. It's something he usually resists, but today, he doesn't seem to even notice. I leave Simon giving Bonnie her breakfast, put the cat carrier on the back seat and drive, probably too fast, to the vet. It's only as I pull into the empty car park that I remember they don't open until nine on a Saturday, and it's only 8.35. Shit. There's a missed call from Simon, and a message saying he got through to the out of hours vet and they can see him straightaway. The trouble is, it's a twenty-minute drive in the other direction, possibly longer if there's a lot of traffic. I turn to look at Oscar. He's lying on his side, drooling, his front legs unnaturally stiff in front of him and the rest of his body twitching violently. Maybe someone will have come in early. I run over to the back door of the surgery and ring the bell. Just as I think no-one's there, a veterinary nurse opens the door, and I burst into tears.

The vet arrives five minutes later, but by that time, Oscar is having continuous seizures.

The nurse comes out to the car with me. Oscar is wrapped in a black plastic bag, which is horrible and disrespectful, but it seemed even worse to put his body in the cat carrier. I call Simon but when I get through, I can't speak, so he guesses.

'We'll bury him under the forsythia bush,' he says gently. 'He liked to sit there.'

I'm about to set off home when I remember I'm supposed to be meeting Anna at ten for a wander round Greenwich

Market before heading to the park for our picnic. Tears streaming down my face, I message her to tell her what's happened and explain that I can't make it. As I press send, I get a horrible feeling that she might be annoyed, especially as this is the second time I've put her off. But a reply comes back almost immediately. *Ah, poor puss. What a shame. Don't worry, we can have a picnic another day xx*

We agree that Bonnie's too young to understand, so we can't bury him while she's around and we can't leave him in the car in this heat, so I smuggle him into the utility room until later.

Poisoning, the vet said. He couldn't be absolutely certain without doing a post-mortem, but all the signs pointed to poisoning. He said there were a lot of things that cats could eat that could make them very ill or even kill them. He asked me about the garden, whether we used slug pellets, whether we grew lilies, and whether we had cut lilies in the house. Apparently, even licking lilies or drinking the water from a vase can be fatal for cats. But we haven't had cut flowers in the house for weeks, and we don't use slug pellets or weed-killer. So we don't know. Maybe he picked something up in someone else's garden. 'Of course,' the vet added, 'it's not impossible that he was poisoned deliberately, but usually when it's deliberate, we have a few cats coming in around the same time. If we do get any more, I'll let you know, and I'll get on to the police. Unfortunately, they rarely catch the sick bastards.'

Once Bonnie's gone down for her nap we wrap Oscar in

his favourite blanket along with his catnip toys and we bury him, marking the grave with a flat grey stone bearing his name, written in marker pen. We don't have a 'funeral', but we stand by the grave for a few minutes, holding hands and talking about what a gentle, affectionate cat he was. We both cry unashamedly, and as we hold each other, I feel a rush of love for Simon, and I wonder what I'll do if I discover he's cheating on me.

CHAPTER TWENTY-THREE

It's over a week since Oscar died but I'm feeling a bit tearful when I come down from putting Bonnie to bed. I read *Cat Heaven* to her as her bedtime story tonight. She's too young for it, really, but if I keep reading it, maybe she'll understand one day. I had to try something – I keep finding her squatting in front of the cat flap, clearly waiting for Oscar to come through it. As I was reading, she put her thumb in her mouth and snuggled down onto her pillow, so I think she found the rhyme soothing at least.

I'm in the garden reading when Simon comes out to say goodbye. He's freshly showered and shaved, which isn't in itself suspicious, but he's wearing one of his best shirts again, and he's looking particularly good tonight. Also, he went for a drink with Marcus just over a week ago, so would he really go again so soon?

'I won't be too late,' he says.

'Where are you going?' I ask as casually as I can, but he instantly looks annoyed.

'I told you, I'm meeting Marcus and—'

'I know that, I meant where? Which pub?'

'Oh, I see. We're meeting at the Gypsy Moth, but we'll probably have one or two there and then go on somewhere else.'

Hmm. So even if I *were* able to get out of the house to check on him, he'd be covered if he wasn't there.

He leans down and kisses me. 'See you later.'

'Yeah, bye.' I turn the page without looking up, pretending to be engrossed. I carry on reading for another five minutes so that I'm sure he's not likely to come back, then I hurry up to the study and take down the box file where I've hidden the parcel. After I've opened it, I fold up all the packaging and bury it at the bottom of my school bag to get rid of later. The set-up instructions are badly written – or badly translated – so I fire up the laptop and search for the YouTube video I watched before I ordered it. *How to set up a hidden spy camera.*

I watch it through, then go back to the start so I can follow it step by step. I download and install the app on my phone, and, pausing the video when I'm not clear what comes next, I gradually work through the set-up. Then comes the moment of truth . . . and yes! It works! The camera's about the size of a walnut and it can be attached to the wall, or to furniture or even to a lightbulb. It's quite unobtrusive. The only problem is the little green light that shows it's recording. I look around for inspiration. Blu Tack! I press a tiny piece down over the light and it does the trick. My stomach churns as I stand on the chair to position the camera on top of the wardrobe, facing the bed. Do I really want to do this?

Back downstairs, I reply to Zoe's latest email, to which she's attached some photos of the beach at Thessaloniki, and a selfie of her and the lovely Dom.

Looks gorgeous! I type, *and so does the beach. Haha :) It's good that you have a couple of weeks to enjoy getting to know the place before you start work.* I ask her about the house where they're staying, the restaurant Dom's working in and how her tan is coming along. Then I tell her that I took her advice and bought the camera. *I've just finished setting it up,* I type. *And now I feel guilty, and a bit sick – I hate snooping like this.*

Her reply comes almost immediately: *Don't feel guilty – you have to know the truth.*

I've been feeling like shit lately, what with losing Oscar, then the camera arriving and the horrible thoughts I keep having since I set it up. So I wasn't particularly looking forward to the barbeque at Ben and Nathan's, but now we're here, I'm quite enjoying it. They're only a ten-minute walk from us, so we can both have a drink without worrying. The party is mainly to celebrate Ben's fortieth, but it's only just over three weeks until the start of the summer break, and with everyone looking forward to six weeks of no school, it's also a nearly-the-end-of-term celebration. Ben's the deputy head. They've all been friends since long before I came along, so I was a bit worried that Sarah might be here, too. But there's no sign of her so far, and I doubt she'll turn up now.

Anna offered to look after Bonnie for us this afternoon, but Amelia, Ben's thirteen-year-old daughter from his brief, misguided marriage, would never have forgiven us if we'd left Bonnie behind. Now Amelia and her friends are entertaining Bonnie and the other two toddlers that are here and they all seem to be enjoying themselves. I drift around, chatting to people I know, mostly other teachers from school. A few of them are still a bit distant with me, but it bothers me less these days. I'm more concerned about making it up with my old friends. Things are much better with Zoe now – we've exchanged a few emails since she arrived in Greece – and I sent a long, grovellingly apologetic email to Tash yesterday, but I've not had a reply yet.

It occurs to me that I haven't seen Simon for a while. I wander around the garden looking for him, then I ask Amelia if she's seen him. 'Yeah,' she says. 'I saw him going out the front door when I went in for some crisps.'

'Really? Where was he going? Did he say?'

She shrugs. 'No.' She laughs at something her friend says and turns back to the game they're playing with the little ones.

'Amelia, sorry, one more thing – any idea how long ago this was?'

'Dunno. About fifteen minutes? Something like that.'

'Okay, thanks.'

As I near the house, Nathan comes out onto the terrace carrying a tray of sausages and I smile when I see the words *Prick with a Fork* emblazoned across his chest. 'Like the apron, Nate.'

He grins back at me. 'It's new. I bought it for Ben, really, but I don't know why – he never bloody cooks!' We both chuckle. I'm about to ask him if he knows where Simon's gone when a notification comes through on my phone. The camera has picked up movement in our bedroom.

'Hey. Emily, are you all right?' Nathan says. 'You've gone white as a sheet.'

'Yes, yes, I'm fine.' My voice sounds as if it's coming from a long way away and my legs feel shaky as I rush past him into the house. 'Just popping to the loo.'

I put my wine glass on the side and hurry up the stairs to their bathroom where I lock myself in and, heart thumping so hard it feels like it's going to burst out of my chest, I put the lid down on the loo and sit. My hand is shaking so much I can barely open up the app. Surely he wouldn't sneak out of a party then run home to shag his mistress? He would have had to arrange it in advance, to *plan* it. No, he wouldn't do that, it's too sordid. He *couldn't*. As I wait for the video to load, I wonder whether the camera could have been triggered by Oscar jumping on the bed, but then I remember we don't have Oscar anymore. I swallow down the lump in my throat. Maybe the camera's faulty. That would explain it. But then the video starts to play and I stare at the screen as she walks into my bedroom and pulls her dress off over her head.

I can hardly breathe and my heart is pumping so hard it almost hurts. But the woman in my bedroom is not Sarah. This woman is nowhere near as tall, and her hair is different. There's something familiar about . . . I cry out and bring my hand up to my mouth as it dawns on me who I'm looking at.

CHAPTER TWENTY-FOUR

Sitting there in Ben and Nathan's bathroom, afternoon sun glancing off the chrome fittings and the sound of conversation and muted laughter rising up from the garden below, I wonder how I'm going to hold myself together enough to go back downstairs. The smell of barbecue smoke and charred sausages drifts through the open window, making me feel nauseous. I'm gripping my phone too tightly. How could I have not seen this going on right under my nose? With a trembling hand, I press pause. Do I really want to carry on watching? Do I want to see my husband fucking Anna in our bed? Part of me wants to throw the phone down the loo and run. Out of this room, out of this house, and to keep running home so I can crash in there and confront them. I think back to her offering to look after Bonnie today. Maybe if I'd agreed to that, he would have made some excuse to go home and check on her. I wonder how many other times he's been there with Anna while I've been at school, wondering why I can't find him. *Bastard.* And no wonder Anna was happy for me to borrow her car to follow him. She must have thought it hilarious that I suspected him of being with Sarah. They probably laughed about it together. For a moment, I feel so awful I think I'm going to pass out, but I manage to get to the basin and splash some water on my face, which makes me feel better. But when I catch sight of myself in the mirror, I'm shocked by how red and blotchy my skin looks. It's bright red from the neck up, as though I've being scalded.

I sit back down and stare at the frozen frame for a full minute or more. Anna, in my bedroom, in her bra and knickers. The underwear isn't particularly sexy, which surprises me, given that she must have known she was going to have sex with my husband today. Or maybe she didn't. Maybe it was spontaneous lust on his part, one of those *I want you so badly, be there in 10 minutes* messages. A tear rolls off my chin and drops onto the phone. I wipe it away with my thumb and press the white triangle to play the video.

The half full glass of wine is where I left it. I pick it up and drink it down in one go, then I go in search of a top-up. My colour is more or less back to normal, I think, and I've stopped shaking. I was so certain I was going to see Simon and Anna having sex in our bed. Thank God it wasn't that. The relief is almost overwhelming, but even so, I still can't quite believe what I've just watched.

Simon is standing at the drinks table, deep in conversation with an attractive-looking blonde in low-cut jeans and a white lace crop-top showing off a flat, tanned midriff. It takes me a couple of seconds to recognise Rachel, the supply teacher. I'm slightly surprised to see her here, but I guess she's been at the school for a few weeks now, so she probably knows everyone fairly well. Simon glances up as I approach, and I'm almost afraid to talk to him in case he asks me why I look so guilty. How could I have thought he'd really leave me and our child at a party to nip home for a quick shag with my friend in our bed?

'Hey,' he says, turning towards me. Then he does a sort of double-take. 'Are you all right?'

'I'm fine, I'm good. Need a top-up, that's all.' I hand him my glass. 'Anyway, where were you? I was looking for you.'

'I went for more ice – Ben asked me to pop round to Sainsbury's, but they didn't have any so I had to go to Waitrose. Why?'

'Why what?'

'You said you were looking for me. What's up?'

I hesitate. If I tell him what I've seen, he'll wonder why I set the camera up in the first place. I need to think about this. I'm relieved it's not what I suspected, but I need to get my head round it before I decide what to do next.

'Oh nothing. I wondered where you were, that's all.'

He nods, picks up a bottle of white from the table, fills my glass and hands it to me, then he turns to Rachel. 'How about you, Rach? Can I tempt you to some more fizz?'

'Ooh, yes please.' She smiles back at him, her lip piercing glinting in the sunlight.

'I'll just pop in and grab another bottle.' He strides off towards the house. Rachel turns to me. 'Hi, Emily. You look nice.'

'So do you.' I smile. Not that she needs telling. She's about my age, but with a flat stomach and breasts that can only be described as perky, and she's showing off both of these attributes to their best advantage today.

'Are you having fun?' she asks.

'Er, yes,' I say, though it seems an odd thing to ask; more the sort of thing I'd say to Bonnie.

'That's good.' She drains the last few drops of her drink, glances around the garden. 'How's your little girl?' she says eventually.

'Oh, she's having a great time. I think the teenagers have adopted her.'

'Good,' Rachel says. 'Cool.' Her gaze keeps darting towards the house, and I realise she's waiting for Simon to come and rescue her. I've come across this before – non-mothers who think the only thing mothers can (or want to) talk about is their children.

'Well, nice to talk to you, Rachel,' I say as I see him returning with a bottle of Prosecco. I touch him on the arm as he pours them both a glass. 'See you in a bit.'

'Yeah, sure,' he says, barely glancing at me.

Later, when we're back home and I'm sitting by Bonnie's cot, waiting for her breathing to fall into that deep, steady pattern that tells me she's properly asleep, I play the video again.

Anna, dressed only in her bra and knickers, walks towards the camera, disappearing momentarily from its range as she opens my wardrobe. Then she appears again with an armful of dresses, including a couple of size 12s I haven't been able to get into since before I had Bonnie. She tries them on, one after the other, turning this way and that in front of the wardrobe mirror. Most of them are too big for her, but the black cocktail dress I used to wear all the time when I went out almost fits, and it suits her. She goes to the little drawer in my jewellery box and tries on some earrings, going for the big silver hoops first. Did she borrow them before? If so, how did she end up putting them in the cat food cupboard? She tries on five dresses and a couple of jackets, then puts everything away again, and then – and this is the bit that really throws me – she pulls back the duvet and climbs into bed. At first, she lies down as if she's going to go to sleep, then she sits up, picks up my book from the bedside table and reads it for – I check the counter on the video – six minutes and fourteen seconds. Then she gets up, straightens the duvet and pillows, and goes out of the room.

PART TWO

CHAPTER TWENTY-FIVE

Anna

At first I just drove past your house a couple of times. It was a lot posher than I expected. You've landed on your feet all right, that's for sure. I wonder how much you paid for the place. Victorian, end of terrace, big bay windows top and bottom, and I knew before I even stepped inside that it would be stuffed with original features and whatnot – cast-iron fireplaces with flowery tiles all around the grate, polished floorboards, fancy plasterwork round the ceiling. Nice.

I like houses. I like those TV shows where people buy up an old house for peanuts then do it up and sell it for a big fat profit. I've always thought I'd be good at that sort of thing if I'd ever had enough money to buy a house. I used to dream that someone would knock on my door one day and say, guess what? Turns out you did have some family after all. An eccentric great aunt who you've never met but who's died and left you two hundred grand. Or maybe three hundred. Mind you, your house will have cost more than that. I looked on Rightmove when I first found out where you lived, and I reckon we're talking a million, easy.

It's lucky that yours is the last house on the street because it's got that alley that runs along the side where you can cut through to the next road. It's a bit dark and overgrown, but you can still walk along it. Not like the little cut-throughs where I live, which are usually full of shopping trolleys and bikes with no wheels and old mattresses. Someone dumped a double mattress the other day, and they'd written on it in marker pen, *all shagged out*. It made me smile, even though I was annoyed. Where I live is scuzzy enough already, without people dumping their old crap right outside your door.

So I walked along past the side of your house, to where it joins up with another alley where you all put your wheelie bins, the one that runs between your gardens and those on the next road. It was broad daylight, and I reckoned yours was the sort of road where there was probably some sort of Neighbourhood Watch thing going on. But once I saw how easy it would be, I knew I'd come back again, maybe after dark. It was all very well knowing where you lived, but that wasn't the same as actually seeing you.

The next time, I waited until about six when it was starting to get dark. I walked past the front of your house first, and yay! You'd left the shutters open. They're nice, those wooden shutters, aren't they? I think I heard someone call them plantation shutters. Cost a fortune, apparently. But it looks to me like you can afford it, what with two good salaries coming in. Oh yes, I did a bit of research. Followed you to see where you worked, then looked up what teachers earn. And by the look of those cars you both drive, I reckon you're on the higher end of the scale.

There was no-one in the lounge, but there were a couple of lamps on, so I could see in, right through to the other end of the house and even into the garden through the French doors at the back. I checked up and down the street but there was no-one about, so I slipped down the cut-through and into the alley that runs between the gardens. It stunk a bit as I squeezed past the bins, but there was a good view from there. I felt a bit nervous, though I was fairly sure you wouldn't be able to see me from the house as long as I was careful to duck down behind the wall every time I took a drag of my cigarette. I was just wondering how long I could get away with staying there, only partly hidden by a tall, bushy shrub, when I saw him, your husband, come into the room and sit on the sofa. Then you came in, and my heart started beating faster as you walked towards the French doors. I was about to jump down and run for it when you reached up and pulled the curtains across, throwing the lawn into darkness.

I watched you quite a lot at first, especially when you'd just had Bonnie. I hadn't even realised you were pregnant. Can you believe that? I just thought you were podgy. Then one day, when I'd not been round for a few weeks, I was just parking up, debating whether to creep down the alley and look in the back or wait in the car to see if you put the front room light on, when I saw you – you and him – coming down the road, pushing one of those fancy pushchairs. I thought you must be looking after someone else's kid at first, then I realised you weren't fat anymore.

What a shock. I went a bit shaky as I watched you lift Bonnie out and jiggle her about while he folded up the push-chair. At that point, I couldn't tell whether she was a boy or a girl because you had her all wrapped up in a white shawl. Once you'd disappeared inside, I made my way to my little spot behind the wall at the back of your garden. I'd only been there a few minutes when your next-door neighbour came down the path to put some bottles in the recycling. My heart wouldn't stop hammering and I swear to God I thought he'd hear it. I kept dead still, scared to even breathe in case he spotted the movement. But he must have been blind as a bat because he came out of his back gate and stood not three feet away from me as he chucked his bottles in the bin, then he turned and went back up the garden path, whistling through his teeth. My palms were sweating and the adrenaline that was pumping round my body was making me feel a bit shaky, so I almost climbed down and went back to the car, but then I saw you come into the room with the little one resting on your shoulder. I still couldn't see whether it was a boy or girl, but I could tell it wasn't very old. A few weeks, maybe? A couple of months?

I wasn't sure how I felt about you having a baby, and so I made myself do what Pete, the only one of the therapists I ever liked, used to tell me to do – wrap the thought in a bit of brown paper and tuck it away to unwrap when I feel ready to have a proper look at it.

I used to think I'd like to have kids. Not loads of them. Not so many that some of them get left out all the time. But turns out I can't have them anyway, not now, so no use in thinking about it. Not that I've ever met a bloke I'd consider having kids with in the first place, but it would have been nice to have had the choice.

Even though I didn't know what you'd had, next time I was doing the rounds of the charity shops, instead of concentrating on finding vintage clothes or other stuff I could sell on eBay, I found myself looking at baby stuff. I found this beautiful little Babygro. Italian, I think, because it said 'Bellissima' in gold thread on the label. It was lilac, soft and velvety with a silky collar, fancy stitching across the chest and around the cuffs, and clusters of flowers and butterflies embroidered all over it. It was the most beautiful thing I'd ever seen. I wasn't sure about the colour, so I asked the assistant, who was about ninety, 'Do you think that colour would be all right for a boy? Or is it only for a girl?'

'No, love,' the woman said. 'That'll do a boy or a girl, that will, and it's lovely quality. Hardly been worn. Cost a bomb if you bought it new.' She felt for the price tag and looked over her glasses. 'Two pounds fifty. You've got a bargain there.'

'Yes,' I said. 'I'll take it. It'll do for my nephew.' Don't know why I said that. I think I wanted to make it real, give myself a reason. I handed over the money, still not really sure why I was buying it, or if I'd ever be able to give it to you. I hoped the woman wouldn't ask me any details, like how old this 'nephew' might be, or what his name was.

As I put it in my bag, I found myself thinking back to my second foster home. I was really happy there. Not that I was unhappy with Gillian and Mike, but after it all went pear-shaped, they couldn't cope with me anymore, so I ended up at the children's home until Janet offered to take me. She was the best foster mother ever. I wanted her to be my real mum. Janet specialised in *troubled young people*, but she took babies as well, and there was this one particular baby, Curtis, he was called. He had huge, glistening brown eyes and dark, nut-brown skin that would have gone lovely with the lilac. It'd be too small for him, though, because I think he was four or five months old when we got him. Curtis and me liked each other a lot. He was with us for about six months, I think. Maybe a bit more. Janet had a playpen in the corner for the little 'uns, and when I came home from school, Curtis would pull himself up by the bars and put his arms out for me to pick him up. The other girls, Jess and Becky, were jealous because I was the only one he'd go to. They both wanted to cuddle him; Janet would have a right go at them for picking him up all the time. He used to cry and put his arms out to me instead.

Once, Becky was holding him too tight, trying to keep him on her lap when he was trying to get down. 'He's not a bleedin' pet rabbit,' Janet told her. 'So stop pawing at him and leave the poor little mite alone for five minutes.' Becky said it wasn't fair – why should I be allowed to play with Curtis and she wasn't. 'Because Anna's nearly fifteen and you're only twelve,' Janet said. 'And because Anna doesn't treat him like a sodding toy!' Becky flounced off to the telly room and I felt well pleased with myself. I was special. I was mature and responsible enough to be trusted. I could be like a third mum to Curtis. Obviously, Janet was his second mum. I'm not sure what happened to his first mum. She might have been a druggie – a lot of them were. I picked Curtis up and covered his plump cheeks with kisses while he grinned and burbled at me. Janet smiled as she poured the batter into the tray of sausages for toad-in-the-hole. 'Don't get too attached, love.'

Then I came home from school one day and he was gone.

I cried my eyes out when she told me. He'd gone to his 'forever home', she said. She sat me on the sofa in the lounge and brought me a cup of sweet tea. I asked her why this couldn't be his forever home. 'Well,' she said, 'for a start, I couldn't give him the life his new mum and dad can so it wouldn't be fair on him, but also, there's other babies need temporary care, so we have to make room for the next one.' She looked at me and her face softened. 'I know it's especially hard for you, Anna, and I know how much you love the little 'uns, but this is how it works.'

Deep down I always knew Curtis would be adopted, but I blanked it out because I loved him so much and he loved me. I don't think it would have been so bad if she'd told me he was going, but Janet said the social workers wouldn't let her say anything. They thought that, because of what happened before, it would be best to keep it quiet until after. Thinking back now, I can hardly believe they were so stupid as to think that doing the same thing again would be a good idea. Fucking idiots. They wouldn't tell me where he'd gone, so I couldn't even go and give him a kiss goodbye. I used to lie awake at night, wondering if he was sad because I wasn't there, or whether he thought I didn't love him.

A few weeks after Curtis went, Janet said she had a lovely surprise for us all. We were getting a new baby – a girl, this time. She was ten weeks old and she was called Alice. Janet made a big point of telling me how much she was relying on me to help out with the new baby, seeing as how I was so responsible and good with the little ones, but that I wasn't to get so attached to this one, because she was a pretty little thing and probably wouldn't be with us for long.

I didn't think she was pretty at all. I thought she was ugly. She had hardly any hair, so she looked bald, especially as she had really bad cradle cap, so her head was covered in a thick, orange crust which Becky used to pick off when no-one was looking. She had pale skin that looked almost translucent, and she used to scream her head off every time Janet put her down.

One day, I got sent home from school early because I wasn't feeling well. My periods were so bad I used to feel like I was dying when I came on. It was only about half two, so Alice was in her pram in the lounge and Janet was in the kitchen making a cake for Jess's birthday. Janet took one look at me and frowned. 'Time of the month?'

I nodded miserably, biting my lip to stop myself from crying. Janet rinsed the flour off her hands and went to the locked cupboard where she kept all the medicines. 'There you are, lovey.' She handed me two Feminax and a glass of water. Then she filled the kettle. 'Let's get you a nice hot water bottle, then you can get yourself off to bed.'

'Thanks.' I swallowed the pills. They were the only thing that even touched the pain, and they worked fairly quickly.

Janet filled the hot water bottle, slipped it into one of her home-made covers and handed it to me. 'There we are, chicken, we'll soon have you feeling better.'

I took it and held it against my cramping belly. There was no point in me trying to go up to bed yet, because the pain was so bad I could barely walk. 'I'll just sit here for a few minutes,' I said. 'Until they start to work.'

'All right, lovey. Listen, I need to pop to the corner shop for some more icing sugar. I'll literally be five minutes. Can you keep an ear out for Alice, for me? Just in case she wakes up.'

'Okay,' I said.

By the time Janet had taken her apron off and put her shoes on, the cramps had started to ease off, so when she left, I got up and wandered along the hallway. I was going to go into the telly room to see what was on, but I heard Alice shuffling about in her pram so I went into the lounge. She was lying on her back, looking up at me. I wanted to like her, but all I could think of was that she pushed Curtis out, that she was a replacement. She started to cry, and I went to pick her up but she went all stiff so I couldn't cuddle her properly, and she just screamed because it was me instead of Janet. So in the end, I laid her back down in her pram. But she carried on screaming. I watched her for a bit, then I picked her up by her ankles and I spun around, holding her out, like in the playground when you're with your friend and you hold each other's wrists and you go round faster and faster until it feels like you're not even doing it yourself.

Alice looked a bit shocked as she slid through the air, but she stopped crying. I didn't do it for long, and when I started to get really dizzy, I slowed down and put her back in her pram quickly before I fell onto the sofa. A couple of minutes later, Janet came back.

'She was crying,' I said, 'so I picked her up.'

'Thanks, chicken. She seems okay now, doesn't she? I'm glad you're getting to like her a bit more.'

'I think I'll go up to bed, now,' I said.

I don't know why I did it. I just remember feeling really angry with both of them, Janet and Alice. I don't think I wanted to hurt her. I was just taking it out on her, and I wanted to see what would happen, but nothing did.

Alice got adopted a few months later. I still didn't like her.

I was amazed that no-one spotted me hanging around your house so often. If you *do* have Neighbourhood Watch round here, they're bloody useless. I suppose it's not like I was there every week, but I was there a lot. I've stood the other side of your garden wall in every weather, on and off more than a year, and I've watched your little girl grow from a newborn into a toddler. I was a bit hurt that I never saw her wear that Babygro, though, and I know you got it because I saw you pick it up off the doorstep. Maybe you put her in it and I just didn't see. I wasn't there much over last summer, partly because I was working weeknights then, as well as weekends. But also it's harder to hide when it's light until ten o'clock and everyone's out in their gardens, so I just drove past from time to time. Then around the start of the new year, I thought, this is it. If I don't do it now, I never will. I didn't know how I was going to approach you or what I was going to do. All I knew was, I had to know you, be part of your life. I wanted a different life to the one I've been living – a crappy job in a pub; a crappy flat in a crappy area where the dogs just shit on the pavement. Same as all the other crappy jobs and crappy flats I've had since I was sixteen. But look at you, Emily. Just look at you.

So I kept going back to my hidey hole at the end of your garden, standing there smoking, watching you and Bonnie as you came and went. I cut down my shifts at the pub to three nights a week, plus the occasional lunchtime, so that made it easier to keep an eye on what you were up to. I thought it would be harder when you went back to work because you weren't getting home until five or six, then as soon as it was dark, you shut all the blinds and curtains. It was a good few weeks before I realised that you were home on Mondays and Fridays, so I guessed you'd gone part time. You were still out quite a bit, though, weren't you? Coffee with the yummy mummies, swimming and yoga with the little one. *Mum and toddler yoga*, it said on the notice, so if I'd wanted to join your yoga class, I'd have had to borrow a toddler. I couldn't afford fifteen quid a time, anyway. I spent weeks working out how I was going to approach you. I kept trying to imagine what would happen if I went up and knocked on your door, but I wouldn't have known what to say. I thought about just coming right out and introducing myself, but apart from the fact that it'd give you a massive shock, I wasn't sure I wanted to disclose that straightaway. Better to get to know you first. I was going to knock on your door one day, though. I was going to see inside that fancy house of yours, and I was going to get a proper look at your baby.

Then one day you came home with a little grey-and-white cat, Oscar – I heard you calling him. Such a sweet thing. Partial to cheese and onion crisps – I bet you didn't know that about him, did you? I only know because I was eating crisps one night while I was watching you and your husband drinking wine on your massive sofa, and your cat jumped up on the wall next to me. He rubbed his cheek against my hand, and then he started nosing at my crisps, so I began feeding them to him – he loved them! I reckoned he'd come to me just for my crisps, but there would probably be other stuff he'd like even more. Tuna, maybe. That was when I came up with a neat little plan. A good way of getting your phone number, and a legitimate reason to come to your house.

I had a cat once, when I was still at Gillian and Mike's. Tiger, she was called, because of her black stripes. She wasn't much more than a kitten when I found her cowering behind the garages on my way home from school. She was all wet and bedraggled, and she looked really scared, but after I crouched down and talked to her for a bit, she started sniffing my hand, and then she came over to me and I picked her up. She let me carry her all the way back to Gillian's. She didn't have a collar, so Gillian thought she was a stray. Gillian said that as long as I fed her and cleaned out her litter tray, I could keep her. I did exactly as I was told, I fed her twice a day, washed up her bowl and emptied her litter tray every morning. I bought her catnip mice with my pocket money and played with her every night after school. But then on Christmas Eve, she got run over.

Oscar was a pretty cat, and so friendly. Of course, by the time he came on his little visit to my flat, he was already used to me, so it was easy to get him to come to me. I fed him bits of tinned tuna for three days beforehand, so as soon as he saw me, he was miaowing for his treat. I gave him a couple of bits from my hand, then I put some on the ground, and while he was snaffling those up, I picked him up, popped him into the holdall and zipped it up, leaving a two-inch gap so that he could breathe. It was the big holdall I used to use for taking my washing to the launderette. I thought it would be less noticeable than a box or a cat-carrier. It's big enough for him to turn around in, and he wouldn't be able to get out while I was driving, so it was safe. I just had to hope I could get him to the car without anyone hearing his loud miaows. I smiled as I settled him in the footwell on the passenger side, because when I got home with him, I would have to literally let the cat out of the bag.

It was nice having a cat again, even if it was only for a few days. I had to take off the collar you bought him, obviously. I think he was relieved to get rid of it, as it happens. He seemed to sort of stretch his neck, like he was enjoying the freedom. I bet you thought he'd be pining for you, but after the first fifteen minutes or so, he settled down happily in my flat, and by the time I'd had him a few days, I'd grown attached to him. I'd have liked to keep him, but that would have *defeated the object of the exercise*, as one of my social workers used to say.

It was two days before you put the flyers up. And there it was in black and white: your phone number. And his, I suppose, your husband's. I guessed the first one on the flyer was yours, but even if it turned out to be his, I'd end the call and he'd assume it was a wrong number. I had to make it convincing, so I waited another three days before I called you. At least, I waited three days before I said anything – I couldn't resist calling a couple of times before, just so I could hear your voice. You sound so posh! Not surprising, I suppose, but it was still a bit of a shock. Better for me to hear you for the first time while I'm sitting safe at home, because I didn't know how I was going to react when I saw you in the flesh.

The day I brought him back, I was a mess. I'd barely slept the night before, because I knew I was going to call you in the morning. Then when we actually spoke ... well, my heart was going like the clappers – I thought I was going to pass out. I was scared you were going to insist on coming to pick him up, and then there would be no reason for us to meet again, but it was easy to persuade you to let me bring him to yours. I was so nervous, I actually threw up. Can you believe that?

One of the first things I noticed was that you still had that scar. You'd obviously tried to cover it up with make-up, but it was wearing off by the time I knocked on your door. I could see it clear as anything, just above your jawline. It's quite distinctive, shaped like a horseshoe. That was useful. At some point, you were bound to ask how I'd found you – I could say it was a coincidence: I found your cat, and when I brought him round, I recognised you by your scar.

I wondered if somehow you might recognise me. I know it was stupid, after all these years – the last time you saw me, you were only two and a half. The odd thing was, at one point, you asked if we'd met before, and I looked at you, willing you to remember.

It felt like I'd waited a long time to be inside your house. It looked just like I thought it would: big rooms, big windows and high ceilings with that fancy plasterwork round the edge, all cherubs and bunches of grapes. Deep, squishy sofas in the lounge and a kitchen that's almost as big as my flat. But you seemed to take it all for granted. I was glad you weren't stuck-up or anything, but you had that same attitude that all spoiled rich girls have, like you're *entitled* – the lovely house, the career with a pension, the drop-dead gorgeous husband – if you like that sort of thing – and the sweet little baby. You take her for granted, you know. Children are a gift, a blessing. But all you ever do is moan – you can't go out with your mates like you used to; you didn't get much sleep because she woke up crying in the night; you can't get things done because she needs entertaining. Honestly, why did you have a baby if it was going to bother you so much? All right, I know you didn't have experience with babies, but you must have known *something* about what was involved? I'm not saying I'm an expert or anything, but you don't have to spend much time in the same house as a young baby to know that they cry a lot. Gillian and Mike looked after a lot of babies, as did Janet, though I can't remember them all.

She's beautiful, your Bonnie, a real angel. There was a girl at Greenfield House called Bonnie, but she was a right cow, always shouting and kicking off, always nicking everyone else's stuff. I felt a bit sorry for her, though. Her dad killed her mum, so he was in prison. I wonder if it's better to have a dad who's alive but killed your mum, or have no dad at all? At least your dad's still alive, even if he did walk out on your mum. I suppose it depends on what the dad was like. Mike would have been nice as a real dad. The main thing I remember about him is that he used to make tea for all us kids on Sundays. There would be sandwiches, but he'd make butterfly cakes and shortbread biscuits himself, and there would be shop-bought cakes as well; Battenberg, French Fancies and little meringues. As long as we ate at least one sandwich, he'd let us eat as many cakes and biscuits as we wanted. He used to wink and say *Don't tell the boss* every time he offered me another cake, but when I think about it, Gillian must have known and pretended not to notice.

They were nice to me, Gillian and Mike, and they liked me at first, but I got too much for them in the end. They didn't tell me it was going to happen, so I never even got the chance to say goodbye. I came home from school one rainy, windy afternoon in November, and you were gone.

Gillian was on the phone and didn't hear me come in, so I didn't even get a warning. I went to the TV room first, as usual, but there was no-one in there, so I went upstairs to the bedroom we shared. All your stuff was gone. Your little bed had been stripped and the shelf where you kept your teddy bears was empty. At first, I thought you were playing a trick on me, that I'd find you hiding in the wardrobe with all your toys packed around you. You used to do that sometimes. But you weren't in the wardrobe. Or under the bed. I went thundering down the stairs and into the lounge where Gillian was still on the phone. She took one look at me and I could tell by her face, she'd guessed I'd been up into the bedroom. 'Where's Emily gone?' I said.

'I'll call you back,' Gillian said into the receiver. 'Yes, she's just come home from school. We haven't told her yet.' She hung up and put her arm out as she came towards me, smiling. 'Come and sit in the kitchen with me, poppet,' she said, sliding her arm around my shoulders. 'How about some hot chocolate?'

She pulled out the heavy wooden chair and I sat at the table. Gillian was being especially nice to me; I could tell by the way her voice had gone all soft as well as the fact that she was making me hot chocolate on a Monday afternoon – that was usually a Saturday night treat. I waited until she put the mug in front of me. Then she got the treats tin down from the top cupboard and took the lid off. 'Go on,' she said. 'Quick, before the others get home.'

I knew I was getting special treatment, and I liked it, but I also knew that there must be a reason. I took a Wagon Wheel from the tin and, as Gillian nodded encouragement, I unwrapped it and took a bite. I'd planned to wait like a good girl until Gillian was ready to tell me what I wanted to know, but I had a bad feeling. I blew on the surface of my hot chocolate and took a sip. I don't know what I thought she was going to say, but despite the bad feeling I had, I didn't think for a second that you might actually be gone for good. So I asked her again. 'Gillian, where's my sister?'

I waited while Gillian stirred her tea and lit a cigarette, probably trying to get her reply straight in her head before she dropped the bomb. 'You remember that nice man and lady who came to tea a few times? The ones who took you and Emily to the park a little while ago?'

I nodded, mouth full of Wagon Wheel.

'Well . . .' She took a big drag of her cigarette, then muttered something under her breath. It sounded like, *God, I hate this bit.* 'They don't have any children of their own, and so . . .' she took another puff on the cigarette, 'so, from now on, they're going to be Emily's new mum and dad.'

It really was like a bomb going off. It was as though everything stopped. I remember thinking I ought to swallow the chewed-up Wagon Wheel I still had in my mouth, but I couldn't move. You'd gone. You'd got a new mum and dad, and I'd lost my baby sister.

I remembered them. The man had a beard and was quite smiley, and his wife was tall and really pretty, like a model. I'd heard Gillian and Mike talking about them. *The Masons,* they were called. No-one told me exactly why they'd come to tea, or why they took us to the park that day, but I could see they were more interested in you than they were in me. For some reason, them taking us out made me think of our mum and dad. The whole time we were out, I felt really, really sad. Then when Mr Mason asked me what was wrong, I started to cry, but I didn't know how to tell them it was because I wanted my mum and dad. We were in the cafe at the time, and they'd bought us both an ice-cream, so it seemed rude to be thinking about our real mum and dad. So I said, 'Nothing.' But I couldn't stop crying, and when they asked me again, I said the same thing. I think they were getting annoyed with me then. Nana – our dad's mum – used to say that nobody liked a crybaby, so that's probably why they didn't take me as well. I vaguely remember asking Gillian once if she thought the Masons hadn't wanted me because I'd spent the whole outing in tears, but obviously she wouldn't have told me, even if it *was* that. She said they wanted only one child, but maybe they decided that after they'd met me. I didn't blame them. You were prettier, blonder, cuter and little more than a baby. Why would they want me?

Linda, my latest social worker, said I wasn't allowed to come and see you because they lived miles away, in London, and anyway, you needed to settle in. I thought that meant they might let me see you later, but then I got a new social worker and every time I asked, she said it wasn't something she could do anything about, so I should try not to think about the past and just concentrate on getting on with my new life. But I didn't know what my new life *was*. Gillian and Mike were foster parents, and I knew that was a job, and that children didn't stay with them for ever.

I have some memories of our real mum and dad but not many. I remember the day they brought you home from the hospital, though. You were really, really little, like a doll. I wanted to hold you but Dad said no at first, then Mum said I could as long as I was sitting in an armchair and was careful to support your head. Dad took a photo. I don't know what happened to it, but I can see it clearly in my head. I was wearing blue denim dungarees with a pink T-shirt underneath, and my hair was tied back in a ponytail. I was sitting in this big, brown armchair and you were resting on a cushion on my lap, wearing a pink Babygro with a big yellow smiling sun on the front. I remember how the weight of your head felt on my arm, and how it felt all warm. 'Nice big smile,' Dad said as he got ready to take the picture. 'But be careful. Don't forget her head's still wobbly.' In the photo, I was looking down at you, smiling.

Our dad used to fix people's cars outside our flat and Mum used to have a go at him because he always had engine oil on his hands and sometimes he'd walk it in on the carpet. He smoked a lot, and he always smelled of cars and fags. I started when I was twelve. I think the main reason was I wanted to smell that smell again to remind me of Dad. Mum smoked too, but not as much as Dad. She drank more than he did, though. He liked beer, and she liked wine – you take after her there. Sometimes, if I woke up in the night, like if I had a nightmare or something, she'd come and settle me down again but she didn't look or sound or smell right because she was pissed. They used to have a lot of rows, but then they'd make up again and be all lovey-dovey, and I'd have to take you out in the garden to play while they went for a 'lie-down'.

They put your cot in my bedroom. You weren't in it at first because you were in their room, and I remember being jealous that you got to be in with them. I used to climb into your cot and pretend I was the new baby who everybody liked best, but then one day I fell asleep in there and Mum shouted that I'd break the bloody thing and I was never to do it again. When you started sleeping in it, I remember thinking there was loads of room for both of us and it wasn't fair that I wasn't allowed. 'You're a big girl,' they kept telling me. 'Why would you want to sleep in the baby's cot?' I knew why, but I didn't know how to explain. I wanted to be adored like you were. I wanted Mum to lean over the bars and smile at me, and to give me so many soft toys that there was hardly room for me in the middle, and to sing that song she used to sing to you.

I wanted to be her sunshine, her only sunshine.

Even with all the toys you had in your cot, you still wanted more. I didn't have many soft toys – I'd mainly grown out of them – but I still had my panda, and I used to let you play with him. Then one day, you wouldn't give him back. Mum tried to take him off you but you hung on tight and wouldn't let go, so she told me to let you have him because you were only a baby and I was a big girl. It wasn't fair. You always got what you wanted, and I never did. Or when I did, I never got to keep it. You don't know what it's like to lose everything you care about. Your shiny new dad might have left you when you were a teenager, but at least you had him until then. And you still have a mum, even though you don't seem to appreciate that. You should think yourself lucky. You take everything for granted, Emily. Including me. You think you can just drop me when an old friend comes along, then pick me up again when you feel like it. Well, I don't like being taken for granted. It hurts. That's why I wanted to hurt you. It was just a shame poor Oscar had to suffer because of it. But that was your fault, Emily. No-one else's.

*

After we'd been at Gillian's for a while, I started to think we might be all right without our parents. Gillian and Mike were lovely, and Nana used to come and see us sometimes, although all she did was cry. She died not long after you left. All I can remember about her now is that she was always smoking, like Dad, and she coughed a lot. I missed Mum and Dad, but at least you liked me more after they died than you did before, and I knew I had to look after you. I think I understood that we might not be with Gillian for ever, but it was a shock to lose you so soon. And after you left, I killed any chance that Gillian and Mike might want to keep me. I don't know why I did the things I did. It was stupid, and I knew I was making myself more and more difficult, but I couldn't stop. I started taking things. Food, usually – biscuits, crisps – the sort of things we were supposed to ask for instead of helping ourselves. It wasn't because I was hungry, it was more because it was easy; because I *could*. I started wetting the bed. The first couple of times, it was a complete accident and I cried, partly because I thought I'd get in trouble and partly because I was embarrassed. But Gillian was so nice about it. She took me to the bathroom and showered all the wee off me, then she changed the sheets and found me clean pyjamas before tucking me in again. 'Don't you worry about it, my love,' she'd say. 'You're not the first bedwetter I've had, and you won't be the last. You'll grow out of it, I promise.'

Sometimes, I'd wake up as I started to wee, and I could probably have stopped but I wanted Gillian to put me in the bath and wrap me up in a warm towel and give me a cuddle, so I just did it in the bed. It was fine for a while, but then I could tell Gillian was getting fed up with it. She started waking me up to have a wee before she went to bed, but I was sleepy and grumpy and I didn't want to get up, so I started not really caring, just wetting the bed almost every night. Gillian never told me off, but she stopped being so nice about it. When I think about it now, I'm surprised she put up with it as long as she did. But apart from bedwetting, I wasn't too bad at first, especially the first year or so after you went. I was on best behaviour most of the time. I thought that as long as I wasn't a crybaby, someone else might want me.

It must have been hard for Gillian, especially as there were usually at least four of us in the house at a time. Some only stayed a week or two, but some were like me, long term. There was a boy called Andrew who I didn't like because he took over everything. He chose what telly we watched, what videos we put on, what games we played. He'd take any toy he wanted, whether anyone else was playing with it or not. He pushed me away from the easel once, so hard that I fell on the floor and hurt my elbow. So as soon as he'd finished his picture, I took it off the easel and tore it up because I was angry and it wasn't fair, so of course I was the one who got into trouble. I should have told Gillian that he'd pushed me over, but I didn't want to be a telltale. The worst thing was when we were out in the garden. He kept picking up stones and pretending he was going to throw them at the windows. He kept saying, *Shall I break that window? Do you dare me? Shall I?* He kept on and on, and in the end, I said, *Oh do what you like.* So he threw a stone at one of the windows next door, breaking the glass. When Mike came rushing out to see what had happened, Andrew admitted that he'd broken the window, but he said I'd told him to do it. I said he was a liar, but then I realised that, in a way, I *had* told him to do it. I explained that I hadn't thought he'd really throw the stone, but even so, I got in trouble as well. I think it was round about that time I started to become 'difficult'.

By the time I was twelve, I wasn't very nice at all. I kept nicking Gillian's fags, or money out of her purse to buy my own. You didn't have to produce ID back then, and even if the shopkeepers were funny about it, there was always someone who'd go in and get them for you. I got worse as I got older, and I took it out on Gillian, but it wasn't her fault. I was arsey with everyone. I'd do something bad, like eating a packet of biscuits or something, then when I got told off for it, I'd do something worse. But it was only when I started running away that Gillian and Mike said they couldn't cope with me anymore. They were nice about it. They said that maybe they weren't the best foster parents for me now I was getting older, and perhaps I'd be happier in another family. I remember wondering if I could make an effort to behave better, but although a big part of me wanted to stay with them, another part hated them for letting the Masons take you and leave me behind. I think I also hated them for being my foster parents and not my real parents. But there wasn't anyone willing to take me at that point, so I ended up at the children's home.

I had another social worker by then, some posh woman

called Dulcia. She was *really* posh, though – not like you, Emily. You're sort of normal posh – like, you talk nicely and you've got loads of money and a right posh house, but to be fair, you don't try to sound like the queen. Dulcia did, but when she came on her regular visits to see how I was getting on, she tried to make herself talk like me. I used to deliberately swear sometimes just to make her swear, too – in her posh accent. It was hilarious. All her 'I's sounded like 'A's. Once, she asked me what I thought of the food there, and I said it was shite. She said, *What makes you say that, Anna? Surely the meals can't all be shate?*

Shate! Me and Kerry, who I shared a room with, used that for a while – every time we didn't like something, we'd say, *Ooh, A think this is a rate load of shate*. Then we'd fall about laughing.

The trouble with the home was that people used to nick your stuff all the time, but I was only there for a few months because then they said about sending me to Janet's. Apparently there was a girl who'd been with her for four years who'd just moved out into her own flat, so there was room for me if I wanted to give it a try. I thought anything would be better than the crappy home so I said yes. I've told you about Janet, and some of the little kids we had there as well. I know I said they were my real family, but that's because that was how it felt a lot of the time. I really loved Janet. It felt like she *was* my mum, in a way. That's why I told you my mum died when I was sixteen. I was talking about Janet. I remember more about her than about our real mum, and I still miss her.

228

CHAPTER TWENTY-SIX

Anna

It was quite a shock when you confronted me on Tuesday because you're not really a confrontational sort of person, are you? The only other time you've done anything like that is that time you asked me if I smoked. I said I didn't, of course, because it's none of your business, but it pissed me off that it would even enter your head that I'd smoke in front of Bonnie. I wouldn't dream of smoking anywhere near her, and I can't believe you thought I would.

So on Tuesday, I'd just given Bonnie her dinner and she was watching *Paw Patrol* in the lounge when you came home, a bit earlier than usual. I'd only just finished cleaning the kitchen, and I was proud of how it looked. Bonnie had been 'helping' – she has her own little cloth and bucket of water, bless her.

You looked around at the gleaming work surfaces when you came in. 'Anna,' you said, 'you don't need to do all this, especially not in this heat.'

I told you it was fine, and that I did it partly for Bonnie because she loves being my special helper. I saw something flicker across your face, and I'm fairly sure it was jealousy, which is a bit of a laugh – *you*, jealous of *me*!

You were looking at my new hair. I thought that was all that was bothering you at first.

'Nice hair,' you said. 'It's a dramatic change. Suits you, though. Where did you have it done?'

'Same place you go. I told them you'd said how good they were – I figured they'd be less likely to cock it up if they knew you'd recommended them.'

I could see you weren't convinced.

'Did I recommend them? I don't remember telling you which salon I go to.'

I ignored that, turning so that you could see the back. 'They've done a good job, haven't they? I'm really pleased with it.'

You were still looking at me. 'Don't you miss your lovely long hair, though?'

'Not really, 'specially not in this weather. This feels much more *me*.' I waited to see whether you'd say anything about it being exactly the same style and colour as yours. I had the impression that you wanted to, but then you got the wine out of the fridge and said you wanted a quick word.

I'll be honest, I felt my insides go all soft as I wondered what you wanted to talk to me about. I picked up the cleaning cloth again and started rubbing away at a spot on the countertop. With it being only a couple of weeks until the school holidays, I was terrified you were going to say you wouldn't need me for those six weeks. We hadn't talked much about how things would work over the holidays, and I hadn't brought it up because I could see you were getting more and more knackered as it got nearer to the end of term, and I didn't want to hassle you.

You told me to leave what I was doing and come and sit down. There was something in the tone of your voice, so I draped the cloth over the taps and pulled out a chair. 'Is something wrong?'

'I'm not sure how to . . .' you began. 'Oh, sod it. I'm just going to say it. Why were you in my bedroom?'

Ah, so you'd finally realised. I knew you would eventually – I even wanted you to, in a way – but I didn't expect you to confront me like that. 'Sorry?' I said, as if I had no idea what you were talking about.

'Last Saturday. When we were out at that barbecue. I know you were here, trying on my clothes.'

I swallowed. I'm not sure how you knew, but you'd obviously sussed it out somehow. You were staring at me. I couldn't work out what was going through your mind. Did you think I'd been stealing from you? I've never stolen anything from you. I borrowed a couple of things, moved a few things around to see if you'd notice, but I don't think you ever did. You've got so much stuff, Emily. You take it all for granted, don't you?

You took your phone out of your bag and turned it towards me, and I was gobsmacked to see myself on the screen. You filmed me! I didn't know whether to be annoyed or impressed. I watched myself trying on the clothes, looking in the mirror, seeing what I might have looked like, what could have been.

'Anna,' you said quietly. 'Just tell me why.'

I didn't answer at first.

'Why?' you said again.

'I wanted to know what it felt like,' I whispered.

'What it felt like?'

'To be you.'

'Why on earth would you want to know what it feels like to be me?'

'You have everything,' I said. 'You have a family. A lovely little girl, a husband, a beautiful house and a good job. And you had more or less whatever you wanted growing up, didn't you?'

'I . . .'

'Private school, riding lessons, foreign holidays,' I continued, my voice hardening. 'A car for your eighteenth birthday.' It was all stuff you'd told me over these last few months, so you couldn't deny it. 'Do you know what I got for my eighteenth birthday?' I'd raised my voice now. 'I'll tell you, shall I? An abortion.' And to my shame I burst into tears. 'Then an infection, so now I can't have kids. Too much scar tissue.'

You leapt up to put your arms around me, but I pushed you away. I don't need your sympathy. You were sorry, you told me, you had no idea.

'Why would you?' I grabbed a tissue from my bag and swiped at my eyes, composing myself again quickly. I'd learned to never let anyone see me cry and I was gutted that you'd seen me like that, in that weakened state.

'Do you want to talk about it?' you said. You looked genuinely concerned, I'll give you that.

I shook my head more vigorously than I meant to. I never even meant to tell you about the abortion. I don't talk about it, but I suppose it's always there, just below the surface. It happened when I was at Greenfield House – that's where they put us when we were too old for foster care but too young or too stupid to look after ourselves. His name was Connor, and he was one of the support workers. I didn't even like him much, but he said he loved me, so I thought I had to sleep with him. When he said he'd take care of everything, I honestly thought he meant he'd look after me and the baby. I wasn't the sharpest knife in the drawer back then. He made the appointment, drove me to the clinic and told me exactly what to say. He said if I didn't, he'd take me to Beachy Head, push me over the top and everyone would think I was just another teenage suicide.

'Sometimes,' I said, 'it just gets to me, how unfair it all was.'

'How unfair all what was?'

'Your life, my life.'

'I don't understand, Anna. I'm really sorry you missed out, and I'm sorry horrible things have happened to you. But what does it have to do with me?'

I sighed. I knew this moment would come at some point. I'd hoped it would be when I decided the time was right, but now you'd caught me trying on your stuff, I couldn't keep it to myself any longer. 'There's something I need to tell you,' I said.

I knew enough by now to know that you hadn't a clue who I was. 'I should have told you before.' I felt myself clutching at my locket. 'I was going to, but I bottled it.'

'Tell me what?'

I tried to warn you that what I was going to say would be a shock, told you that I'd thought about explaining it all to Simon first. You said I was being melodramatic. You laughed, but it was a nervous laugh. And when I looked at the worried expression on your face, the penny dropped. You thought I was going to tell you something about Simon, didn't you? Did you think I had the hots for your husband? Not a chance. I considered screwing him when I first got to know you and when I was feeling especially angry with you for having everything you wanted. But then I realised, Simon isn't someone you have permanently, anyway, no matter what you tell yourself. I wouldn't have been taking anything from you, so there was no point.

'Okay,' I said. 'What do you know about the first three years of your life?'

'What? Anna, what are you talking about?'

At that point, I wasn't sure if you even knew you were adopted. You'd never mentioned it, and I didn't find anything about it in any of your emails, despite trawling through so many of them that I started to get a headache. I only had your phone for a few hours, but it was long enough to get a fair bit of information. It also stirred up the anger again, the bitterness at the unfairness of it all. That's why I sent myself that message from your phone about coming earlier for lunch that day – I wanted you to feel a bit thrown, like it wasn't all going your way after all. Your inbox told me a lot about you: where you get your hair done, what you like to read, where you like to shop. Honestly Emily, you spend money like water! So many emails with the subject line *thank you for your order*. Sometimes, when I was looking through your phone – the emails, the photos of exotic holidays, glamorous nights out, your lovely little baby – I felt the unfairness of it so deeply that the desire to hurt you almost overwhelmed me. But like I said, at this point, when you'd just confronted me about being in your bedroom, instead of feeling angry at you or afraid for myself, I felt genuinely sorry for you. I sighed. 'Emily, how much did your mum tell you about—'

'Look,' you said, 'just stop playing games.'

'I'm not playing games.'

'Anna!' You banged your hand down on the table. 'What has any of this got to do with you breaking into my—'

'I didn't break in. I used the spare key.'

'Oh, for God's sake, you know what I mean. I'm starting to lose patience now. Are you going to tell me what the hell you're trying to get at?'

'Emily, please. I will, but it's difficult. What did your mum tell you? About your early life?'

'Why are you asking me this?'

'I'm asking because ... because I'm not sure if you know about your parents. Whether they told you that you're adopted.'

'Of course I bloody know I'm adopted,' you snapped.

That was unusual. You weren't usually snappy with me.

'But how do *you* know?' you said. 'I didn't tell you.'

'No, exactly. That's why I thought you might not know.'

'So, who told you? Simon?'

'Emily, listen to me. I know this is going to be hard to believe, but I'm your sister.'

CHAPTER TWENTY-SEVEN

Emily

I just stare at her. It's such a bizarre thing to say, I don't react at all at first. Then I laugh, although even as I'm laughing, I sort of know that she isn't making a joke. Is she trying to throw me off my point, i.e. what the fuck was she doing in my bedroom? Then I think maybe I get what she's trying to do. 'Look, Anna . . .' I stop laughing and try not to sound too angry because it's beginning to dawn on me that maybe Anna is more vulnerable than she looks. I think about how upset she gets if I have to cancel an arrangement, how pissed off she was that day I went to meet Zoe.

'Look, I know we've grown very close, and yes, maybe we've become a bit like sisters, but that doesn't mean you can come into my house when—'

She's shaking her head slowly from side to side, clutching her locket and sliding it back and forth on its chain. 'No,' she says. 'No, that's not what I meant.' She looks at me and there's something so intense in her eyes that I can't look away.

'I don't mean we're like sisters, I mean I'm your actual sister. We had the same mum and dad. We were fostered together and then you were adopted when you were two and a half and I never saw you again. They took you away and you forgot about me. I was your big sister and you forgot I ever existed.' I think I see tears in her eyes but she quickly bats them away so I can't be sure.

Over the next few minutes – or it could be seconds or hours, God knows, because time has gone seriously wonky – a jumble of thoughts and memories and bits of conversation stampede through my head. Then my mind goes blank and I can't feel my body at all. So this is what people mean when they say they feel paralysed. I have to reassure myself that I'm not asleep in bed, dreaming all this. I can see my hands, lying there in my lap like a couple of dead things. I try to move them but I can't. I force my brain back into action. Think, I tell myself. Just think. I'm sitting in my own kitchen, the late afternoon sun is pouring through the window, burning my left arm. My daughter is watching cartoons in the sitting room, my husband isn't home yet. My friend is telling me that I have a sister, and that she is in fact that sister and we were separated more than thirty years ago.

'No,' I say, 'that can't be right.' Suddenly, it's as though I flood back into myself. I can feel my body again. I jump to my feet, knocking the table as I do so. My glass is empty so I go to the fridge for more wine. I grab another glass from the cupboard, then bang it down in front of Anna and fill them both without asking.

'Right,' I take a big gulp, 'you need to tell me what the fuck's going on. I never told you I was adopted – and don't say I must have forgotten because I'm bloody certain that I didn't.'

'You didn't,' she says. 'I already knew. I remember the day they came to get you. At least they never changed your name. You've never told me your middle name either, have you? It's Melissa.'

'You've been poking around my house. That's easy enough to find out.'

'Don't tell me any details, but did your adoptive parents tell you what happened to your parents? *Our* parents. That's assuming they told you the truth, of course.' She says this scornfully.

I don't say anything.

'A car crash,' she says quietly. 'July 1989, first week of the school holidays. It was hot. Like this.'

'Stop it.' I put my hand out in front of me as though to halt the stream of her words. It *was* a car crash, and it was in the summer of 1989. That's all I was told, that and their names.

'You don't believe me, do you? Look, I can prove it. Do you know what you looked like when you were very little? I mean, did your new parents take photos?' She reaches up and unclips the silver chain around her neck. Then she presses her thumb against the edge of the oval locket and it springs open. She passes me the locket. There are two photos inside, two little girls, one with darkish-blonde hair, held in bunches with red bobbles, a gap where one of her

239

front teeth is missing. 'That's me,' Anna says, pointing. I can see the resemblance; even as a child, she had those thick eyebrows. 'And that,' Anna points to the other photo, a much younger child, hair a lighter blonde, cuddling a pink teddy bear, 'is you. You must have been about eighteen months old. Maybe a bit more.' There's a pause and I realise she's looking at me.

'Obviously this was before the crash. I used to have a photo of the two of us together when we were with the foster family – Mike, our foster dad took it – but I lost it when my stuff got nicked in the children's home. It showed your scar. It was still bright red at that point. I'm glad it's faded so much now, but that's how I knew it was you.'

'Sorry?' I'm struggling to take all this in.

'Your scar. That was how I recognised you – remember when I found your cat? As soon as you opened the door and I saw that scar, I knew it was you. We used to call it your lucky horseshoe.'

My hand strays up to my face and I run my fingers along my scar. I used to do this all the time, unable to stop touching the weirdly shiny skin.

'I know it was a coincidence,' Anna says, 'you losing your cat, and me being the one to find him.' Her gaze drifts off to the side. 'But stranger things have happened.' She looks back at me. 'Maybe it was meant to be.'

'How . . .' My voice is barely more than a whisper. 'How did you get this photo?' I don't seem to have the energy to make proper sound.

Anna sighs. 'The locket was our mum's. She used to wear it all the time.'

I'm still rubbing my finger over my scar. 'You couldn't have recognised me by this,' I say eventually. 'I got it falling off a climbing frame when I was three – that was six months after I was adopted.'

'No, you didn't. You got it in the crash.'

She's looking at me, waiting for me to react, but I don't say anything as I try to take this in. Outside, there are children shrieking and laughing in next door's garden. In here, all I can hear is the humming of the fridge, and odd snatches of sound coming from the TV in the sitting room. 'You mean, I was in the car at the time?'

'We both were.' Anna gets to her feet. 'I think you need another drink,' she says, and again I realise I've drunk a glass of wine without registering it.

'It's the only thing of hers I have,' Anna is saying. 'Our parents owed a lot on credit cards, apparently, so everything was sold to pay their debts, and no-one thought to save any of their personal stuff. When they died, our dad's mother – Nana – was still alive, but she was ill and couldn't look after us permanently, though we were with her for the first few days. There were no other relatives.' She gently clicks the locket shut, then she looks at me. 'So you – you and Bonnie – are my only family.'

CHAPTER TWENTY-EIGHT

Emily

I want to believe her. I think I do believe her, but it's so much to take in and I can't think straight right now. I keep looking at her, searching her face for clues. There *is* a similarity in our features, I think. Our eyes are the same colour, and we're not that different in height.

'We're family, Emily,' she's saying again. 'You, me and Bonnie. We're the same blood.'

The words hang in the air. I don't know what time it is, and I'm not sure how long I've been sitting here, but it feels like a hundred years have passed since I came home from school. My head feels like it's going to explode. 'I need to get out,' I say. 'Do you mind hanging on while I go for a walk? I won't be long, but I need to clear my head.'

'Of course,' Anna says. 'It's only just gone six, anyway. Take as long as you need.'

I head towards the high street, but I barely register where I'm going, and I'm not sure how I find myself standing at the railings, looking out over the Thames with the *Cutty Sark* behind me. I keep thinking over and over, *Anna is my sister,* but that doesn't make it any more real. All these years, I've longed for some link, some tangible evidence of who I am, of where I come from. Now here it is, and I can't get my head round it. I take my phone out, instinctively wanting to talk to someone about what's happned. Ironically, when I think of who I want to tell about this dramatic, life-changing and shocking revelation, the person who immediately springs to mind is Anna. She's been my 'go-to' confidante for the last few months, so I naturally think of her first. I look at my watch. Simon's probably in a meeting now; I don't want to tell him this over the phone, anyway. I could message Zoe, but it's not like we can just meet for a drink and chat about it. And Tash never answered my email anyway.

I'm not sure how long I stand there, staring out at the river. It's busy this evening, with a few small boats going up and down; there's a party boat from which music and laughter ring out across the water, and the Thames riverbus service going to and from central London with its mix of commuters and tourists. It's cooler down here by the river, and every so often, there's a slight movement in the air, not quite a breeze, but enough to lift my hair away from my head. I'm conscious of a family standing a few feet away, a man and two women with a little boy of about five, who's holding the hands of both women. The women look so alike, they're clearly sisters, if not twins. 'Okay, Max,' the man says. 'You look after Mummy and Aunty Beth while I go for the ice-creams, okay?' The boy nods, and both women look down at him fondly.

Anna is my sister; she's Bonnie's aunt. We have a birth family.

'But why didn't you tell me?' I say when I'm back at the house. 'Why didn't you say something that first day when you brought Oscar back? We've been friends for months!'

Anna lowers her head. 'I know. I don't know why I didn't speak up before, is the honest answer. I think at first I sort of hoped you'd recognise me – do you remember how you said you thought we'd met before? I really thought you might remember. But then you didn't, and I didn't want to shock you, and then because I didn't tell you straightaway, it got harder and harder.'

But then I remember something. 'You told me your mum died when you were sixteen.'

'I meant Janet, my foster mum. The last one. She was like my real mum, that's why I—'

'Okay, what about your brothers and sisters? Are you telling me I have more siblings somewhere?'

She looks thrown for a moment, then she shakes her head. 'No,' she says, 'it was just us two.'

'So which is the lie, Anna? Are you lying about being my sister, or are the brothers and sisters you told me about just figments of your imagination?'

She's shaking her head. 'Sorry,' she says. 'I don't know why I told so many lies. I don't have any other siblings. Not real, blood siblings, anyway. I was thinking of my foster brothers and sisters. Well, mainly my foster sisters.' She takes a tissue out of her bag and blows her nose, then gets up to put it in the bin. 'There were three of us who were with Janet long term,' she says, sitting down again. 'Me, Jessica Banbury and Becky Williams. I'm still in touch with Jess – only Christmas cards and that. We used to be close, though. Becky died a couple of years ago – cancer, same as Janet. She was only thirty-four – same age as you.' She casts her eyes down for a moment, then sighs. 'You never know what's around the corner, do you?'

I feel sorry for her as she tells me this because she looks genuinely sad, and genuinely sorry for the lies. There's a slightly childlike quality about her sometimes, brought back to me now by the way she uses their full names, like the kids at school do, especially the younger ones. But then that suggests she thinks of her foster sisters as friends, not family. Oh, I don't know. I can't think straight anymore. I can hear Bonnie starting to get agitated in the sitting room. I need to get her ready for bed. I stand up. 'Anna, I'm sorry, I can't get my head round it any more tonight. I think you'd better go home now. I need some time to think about all this. We can talk again tomorrow.'

She looks crestfallen, but I can see she won't argue.

'Okay. I'll just say goodbye to Bonnie.'

We both go through to the sitting room, and I lift Bonnie out of her highchair. Her skin is warm and damp and she smells hot and salty. 'Anna's going home now, sweetheart. Say bye-bye.'

Bonnie furrows her brow and shakes her head. 'No,' she says, and I know it means *no, I don't want Anna to go*, not *no, I won't say goodbye.*

Anna leans in to kiss Bonnie's cheek. 'I'll see you again tomorrow, chick,' she says.

'No!' Bonnie says crossly, rubbing her eyes with her fists.

'You're tired, aren't you?' Anna says. 'So am I.' She pretends to yawn. 'It's nearly my bedtime. And Mummy's bedtime. I'll see you tomorrow after we've all had a nice sleep, okay?'

Bonnie looks at me curiously. I yawn. 'Yes, Mummy's tired too. Tell you what, shall we have a story before bed?'

Bonnie nods and is overtaken by a yawn. Anna smiles and cups Bonnie's cheek. Then she turns to me. 'I'm sorry, Emily. I should have told you straightaway.' She turns to go.

'Bye-bye,' Bonnie says, waving, then she blows a kiss, which I've taught her to do, but which she doesn't usually do without prompting.

I push down another stab of jealousy at how fond Bonnie is of Anna. Who, it seems, is probably her actual, blood-related aunt.

After Anna's gone home and I've got Bonnie off to bed, I don't quite know what to do with myself. I try calling Simon, but he's obviously got his phone on silent, and that's when I remember he said he'd be late again tonight. I think about phoning my mother, but I need to know more first.

I spend so long googling 1989 and different combinations

of words that I'm starting to get a headache. I try *accident +
fatal + car*, then I swap *car* for *motor*, then *accident* for *crash*.
Then I try *road traffic accident* and I add words like *killed*,
deaths and *fatal*. I'm about to give up when I stumble on
the British Newspaper Archive. This looks like it might
be exactly what I need. It's not long before I find what I'm
looking for.

SISTERS SURVIVE TRAGIC CRASH
THAT KILLS PARENTS

*Two young children were plucked from the wreckage of a Morris
Marina on Sunday morning after their parents were killed when
their car left the road and collided with a tree off the B2026
just outside Edenbridge. Robert Clarke and his wife, Elizabeth
Clarke, were pronounced dead at the scene, but miraculously, their
two daughters, Anna, eight, and two-year-old Emily, escaped
with cuts and bruises. The children were treated in hospital but
not detained and are currently being cared for by a relative.*

It's only when I feel the wetness on the back of my hand I
realise I'm crying, although I don't know whether I'm crying
for myself, my dead parents, or for Anna, who was telling
the truth.

When Simon comes in just after ten, I'm already in bed. My
head is pounding and I feel like I could sleep for a week. I
tell him the gist of it, and watch as his eyes widen.

'Wow,' he says. 'That's ... well, it's incredible, to be honest. Do you believe her? Are you sure it's not a wind-up?'

'It's not a wind-up. And why would ...' I flick my head in irritation. 'Oh, never mind. I know it's hard to believe, but it's true. I googled it, found the newspaper report.'

Simon lets out a long, slow whistle. 'Fucking hell. I mean ... sorry, I can't think what else to say. She's your actual sister? Like, same mum, same dad?'

'Yes. My actual sister.'

He shakes his head like he can't believe it either. 'How do you feel?'

'Not great,' I tell him. 'I've got a thumping headache and I feel sick. And I'm tired. Really, really tired. I don't want to talk about it anymore tonight. Can we talk tomorrow?'

He only lingers for a moment. 'If you're sure,' he says. Then he leans over to kiss me, and as he does so, I'm sure I catch the tiniest trace of perfume. My first thought is Sarah, although I've never known her to wear anything other than Dior's Joy. But I'm too exhausted to even think about any of that now. 'I need to sleep,' I murmur, turning my face deeper into the pillow. I hear the bedroom door click shut gently as he leaves.

CHAPTER TWENTY-NINE

Emily

Trying to appear normal as I make Bonnie's breakfast is a struggle. I feel sick and shaky; I think it's a combination of shock and lack of sleep. I was awake all night – I mean literally all night. I don't think that's ever happened to me before. My eyes feel gritty and raw and there's a headache lurking in the background. Reluctantly, I call in to school to say I won't be in. There's no way I can handle it on no sleep. Then I text Anna to say I'm not going in so I won't need her today or tomorrow. I *am* going in tomorrow – I've got to, because I'm helping organise the end-of-term talent show, 'Woodview's Got Talent', a one-off, simplified version of the TV show – but I don't think I want to see Anna until I know we'll have time to talk about all this properly. I really need to get my head round the fact that she's actually Bonnie's aunt before we go any further. I'm not even sure why I need to get my head round it, only that I can't think straight at the moment. Anna replies straightaway: *I understand, but we should*

249

talk soon. I'll come round on Friday morning. I notice she doesn't ask if that's okay, but I guess she's taking charge because I'm not being very proactive. I still can't quite believe she's my sister. We do look similar, I suppose, especially now she's had her hair cut and coloured like mine. Except she's a lot slimmer, obviously.

There are so many emotions tumbling around in my head, but I think what kept me awake last night was anger. While I was lying there desperate for sleep, I couldn't work out who I was more furious with – Anna for not telling me sooner, or my mother for not ever telling me. I wanted to call both of them in the middle of the night to tell them how angry I was. Then I started to feel angry with myself for being angry. After all, I'm the one who's had the privileged life.

As soon as Simon has left for Gemma's with Bonnie, I head over to my mother's, pulling up outside her house just before eight. It's warm already, even at this time in the morning, and I can feel the sweat starting to prickle my armpits. The bedroom curtains are still drawn, so while I wait for them to open, I turn on the car radio and listen to some politician dancing round the question rather than answering it. Which is just what my mother does. Maybe she should have gone into politics.

Ten minutes later, I'm walking up the path. Normally, I'd use my key, but she's not expecting me, and anyway, today I feel even less close to her than I usually do. I ring the bell.

'Emily! Goodness, this is a surprise. Whatever are you doing here at this time in the morning? I'm not even dressed.'

'It doesn't matter whether you're dressed or not.' I barge past her and walk into the kitchen, anger bubbling so hard inside me that I feel it's going to burst out at any moment. 'I need to talk to you,' I say, filling the kettle and banging it back down on the worktop then hitting the switch to turn it on. 'More importantly,' I turn to face her, 'you need to talk to me.'

She looks confused. 'What on earth are you talking about?'

I drag a chair out from under the table and drop myself into it. My whole body is aching with tiredness but I know I won't sleep until I've had this out with her. When I don't answer immediately, she turns to the worktop and starts busying herself with mugs, tea bags, milk.

'Earl Grey or English breakfast? I've got some lemon to go with the Earl Grey if you prefer, or—'

'I really don't care. Whatever you're having.'

She purses her lips and I can see by her expression she wants to make some comment about my rudeness, but she clearly thinks better of it because instead she says, 'Are you all right, darling? You look awfully tired.'

'I didn't sleep last night. At all.'

'Whyever not?' She's looking at me more closely now. 'Are you going to tell me what the matter is, or have I to guess?'

'Why didn't you tell me?' I say it quietly to try and control my voice.

'Tell you *what*, for heaven's sake? Come along, darling, I don't have time for riddles.' She picks up the kettle and pours boiling water into the mugs. 'I have a hair appointment at ten.'

'Cancel it.'

I'm guessing it's my tone that makes her freeze. She actually looks a bit scared now.

'Emily, what—'

'Why didn't you tell me I had a sister?'

The silence that follows is so thick and heavy it almost crushes me. My mother pales. She sways as she sets the kettle back down and reaches for the back of a chair to steady herself, gripping it so hard her knuckles turn white.

'How did you—'

'You've known for all this time that I had a sister, a blood relative out there somewhere, wondering what happened to me.' I'm shouting now, and crying, the tears and words are gushing out faster than I want them to. 'You lied to me about the accident. You knew I was in that car when it crashed.' My hand strays up to my scar. 'You told me I got this falling off a climbing frame! Christ, no wonder I didn't like cars when I was little. You knew I'd seen my parents die.'

She flinches.

'Darling, I . . .' Her voice is barely more than a whisper. She shakes her head. 'How did you find out?'

'Because she's here. Anna. She's the new friend I told you about, the one who looks after Bonnie. We met by accident and she recognised my scar.'

Her eyes widen. She pulls out the chair and sits down. 'How on earth . . . ?' But she doesn't say any more.

'The only person I had left was my sister, and you—'

'Emily . . .' she begins, but nothing else comes.

'I just don't understand how you could split us up without a second thought. No wonder you were so fucking reluctant to talk about it. No!' I put my hand up, palm facing her. 'Do not! Just do not *dare* tell me to watch my language.'

I stop shouting, and the silence rings around us. She just sits there, my mother, staring straight ahead. I notice my car keys lying on the floor, and I don't know whether I dropped them there or threw them. I pick them up.

'I can't do this.' I shake my head. 'Right now I can't even look at you. We need to talk about this again,' I say. 'But not now.' As I leave, I see that her eyes are glittering with tears.

CHAPTER THIRTY

Emily

I wake up feeling like I've had a night's sleep, but then I realise it's still dark. A glance at the clock tells me it's only ten to midnight, so I've been asleep for less than two hours. It's been a tough day, and I'm not sure how I managed to get through it. I feel as if I've been walking around like a zombie all day, and I must have looked like one, too, because first the postman asked me if I was okay, then when I was hanging the washing out, our next-door neighbour said the same thing. He'd said my name a couple of times before I even realised he was talking to me. 'Sorry, I'm a bit preoccupied,' I told him. 'I've got some weird family stuff going on.' Which I suppose is true.

Simon is breathing softly next to me. I don't know what time he came to bed because I came up before ten, barely able to keep my eyes open, and also because I was annoyed with him. We barely talked about the Anna situation the other night because my head was still spinning from her revelation, so I wanted to talk about it when he came home tonight. Then I realise that it wasn't 'the other night' that this all happened, it was actually last night. It seems a lot longer than thirty-odd hours ago that I learned I have a sister. Anyway, when I did bring it up – after it became clear he wasn't going to ask – he just said, 'Yeah, wow. It's one hell of a head-fuck, isn't it? But at least you always wanted a sister, so I guess that's good.' And before I had time to say anything else, he said he had emails he needed to deal with and he disappeared up to the study.

It's unbearably hot in here again. I get up and push the window open a little more, then I slide back into bed, turning my pillow over, so that the cool side touches my skin. I need to sleep if I'm going in to school tomorrow, so I try to focus on my breathing in an attempt to calm my agitated mind. But other thoughts nudge the edge of my consciousness. There's one thing in particular that I can't stop thinking about – myself as a toddler, seeing my parents die. Did I know what was happening? I think about Bonnie being in that situation and the thought physically hurts my heart. She's even younger than I was at the time, and the idea of her being trapped in a car with Simon and me dead in the front . . . it's too awful to even contemplate.

Maybe it's because I go to sleep thinking about it all, but I dream about car crashes. It feels like I'm dreaming the whole night long, dream after dream in which I see Bonnie trapped in her car seat and screaming in terror as the car accelerates over a cliff, or plunges down a ravine, or simply hurtles out of control on a motorway. I wake up sweating, heart pounding, adrenaline flooding my body. I manage to doze a bit after that, but I don't get much more sleep and at a quarter to six, I give up trying.

It's as I'm driving to school that I have what I suppose must be a flashback. It's certainly more than just a memory because I feel it as if it's actually happening now: I'm in the back seat of a car, unable to control anything, and I'm aware of feeling scared at the same time as feeling sick from the smell of the hot plastic seats. We're going really fast, then there's screaming and the car is bumping violently downhill and rolling over so that at one point, I'm upside down. I can feel straps cutting into my neck and chest and I can't breathe. Then I'm the right way up again and the car sort of bounces, then something hits me hard on the side of the face, like a punch, before the car comes to rest at a weird angle.

Suddenly, I'm back in the here and now, inching my way along the A2 in the morning traffic, but my heart is banging against my chest and I'm breathing so quickly I'm starting to feel dizzy. I pull over to the side of the road, gripping the steering wheel so hard my knuckles are white. I'm trembling all over.

I'm still a bit shaky when I arrive at school. The flashback or whatever it was seems to have opened a door in my brain because memories start popping up from nowhere. Just glimpses, really, of what must have been my life before I was adopted, brief but incredibly vivid. In the middle of period two, seemingly with no trigger at all, I have a memory of playing on a rug in front of one of those old gas fires, and a very old lady smoking as she watches me from an armchair. She's wearing pink slippers with little bows in the front. I'll ask Anna about the slippers, but I'm guessing I'm remembering my nana. Unless my brain, which must be struggling under the weight of all this new information, has conjured this up from what Anna told me. But this is closely followed by another snapshot. Again, I'm on the floor, my eyes level with a pair of knees in worn, faded jeans. Then I'm being lifted by the armpits, thrown into the air and caught in big, warm hands, then thrown in the air again. A man's smiling face, a woman's voice, 'Careful! Not so high!'

This is a real memory, I know it is; I'm remembering my mum and dad.

Daniel Ogubo, who is in the middle of reading a poem aloud, stops and looks at me. 'Wassup, Miss? I thought I was supposed to—'

'I'm sorry, Daniel. Carry on. You're doing fine – that last line reminded me of something, that's all.'

I have no idea what the last line was, but the way Daniel turns round and grins at the class, together with the sniggers, whistles and comments, tells me I've strayed into risky – or risqué – territory.

I take a chance, smile broadly and tell them it's not what they're thinking and they must all have filthy minds. More cheering and jeering. They love it.

At the end of the day, as I'm walking across the playground to the car park, I notice a woman with a child in a pushchair.

For a second, I think it's Anna, meeting me with Bonnie, but then I realise how unlikely that is, given that the school is more than six miles from where we live. But then another memory creeps in: I'm in a pushchair, waiting just inside the school gates and searching the faces of the children pouring out into the playground. I'm looking for my big sister.

As I'm driving to Gemma's, I think about the flashback I had this morning. This time, I'm able to simply remember it rather than hear the sounds and smell the smells as though it's actually happening. Although I suppose I'm remembering the flashback, not the accident itself. I force myself to think about it, how the car left the road and rolled over and over before coming to rest at the bottom of the grass bank. I can see my parents in the front, their bodies shaking violently as the car goes over the bumps. Maybe I *am* remembering the accident now. Then another image ripples into my mind: my mother, her head bent at an awkward angle by the greenery that's pushing through the window. There's blood every-where; it's dripping off the leaves.

I take some deep breaths and try to focus on the road. Even though it's a horrible, terrible memory, I'm glad it's there. It's easier to come to terms with something when you feel connected to it instead of simply being told it happened. I just wish I could have remembered some of this before.

CHAPTER THIRTY-ONE

Emily

It's Friday, three days after Anna's revelation, which seems to have opened the floodgates to my memory. Little details are coming back to me: things about the crash, about my birth parents and even about the foster home. I woke up this morning with a memory of the day I was adopted – arriving home with my 'new' mum and dad and being shown my room, which was pink and white and had an enormous doll's house standing in the corner.

Anna arrives at nine on the dot. When I open the door, we both smile awkwardly. We don't speak as she follows me along the hallway to the kitchen. Bonnie's in her highchair, feeding herself porridge and raspberries. She breaks into a porridge-smeared smile when she sees Anna. 'Hi,' she says.

'Hi, my darling.' Anna sounds weary.

Bonnie sucks her spoon clean, then holds her bowl upside down. 'All gone,' she says. At least, that's what it sounds like. I grab a couple of baby wipes and ask Anna if she'd like coffee.

'Please.' She hangs her bag over the back of the chair. 'I'll make it.'

'Thanks.' Only a few months ago, Anna was in awe of the coffee machine. Now she fills the water reservoir, grabs a couple of pods from the top cupboard and slots them into the machine as though she does it every day of her life.

After I've cleaned Bonnie's face and hands and lifted her out of her highchair, setting her free to pull everything out of her toybox, I sit opposite Anna at the table. The rich, smoky aroma of coffee is in the air, reminding me of the many times we've sat in various coffee shops, sharing a slice of cake and chatting as though we've known each other for years. Which I suppose, in a way, we have.

'So,' Anna says, taking a tiny sip. She takes it black now, same as me. 'This is a bit strange, isn't it? You and me having coffee together like normal.'

I manage a smile. 'I was just thinking that.'

The only sound is of Bonnie moving her toys around and occasionally chattering to herself. Then she pushes her favourite yellow truck out of the kitchen and along the hallway, leaving Anna and me sitting in an awkward silence. I get up and go to the cupboard for the biscuit tin, more because I can't think what else to say or do than because I want a biscuit. There's so much I want to say, but I can't make the words come. When I take the lid off and offer the tin to Anna, I sense that she's as relieved as I am to have something to do, even if it's only to eat a biscuit. Bonnie comes toddling back in, eagle-ears having picked up the sound. 'Bibit!' She points at the tin.

Without thinking, I reach for a biscuit to give to her, but Anna says, 'What do we say when we want something, chicken?'

Bonnie looks at her earnestly. 'Peese,' she says beautifully. Anna must have taught her, because I didn't. I feel a double stab of guilt, mixed with regret and jealousy, but I manage to say, 'Good girl', and tell Anna I'm impressed.

'Up,' Bonnie says, pointing. I pull her onto my lap, and she settles to eating her oat cookie. Bonnie being there makes things easier, and we both start talking to her, then about her, then about other things, stupid things, like how hot it is outside compared to yesterday, and whether it's likely to be as hot again tomorrow. Then there's a lull and I say, 'Are we ever going to talk about this or what?'

'Yes, we should,' Anna says, then sighs deeply. 'Are you still angry with me?'

'I'm not angry with you,' I say automatically. Then, 'Well, not anymore, anyway. I was angry at first, I guess. I still don't really get why you didn't tell me sooner. It just feels bloody weird. We've known each other, what? Over four months now, and we've talked and talked, including about our families. How could you *not* tell me?'

She licks the tip of her finger and presses it against a few stray crumbs on the table. 'I know. I should have told you. But like I said, I was worried about how you'd take it. And don't forget, even though we talked about our families, you never told me you were adopted, so how was I to know whether you even knew? What if your adoptive parents had never told you? Can you imagine what a shock that would have been?'

I concede that she has a point.

'I didn't want to risk upsetting you,' she continues. 'I know I *have* upset you, but I honestly didn't mean to. I kept hoping you'd mention it so I could be sure.'

'And then you'd have told me?'

She nods. 'I think so. Although I'm not saying I wouldn't have lost my nerve – it's a big thing to tell someone.' She's looking right at me now. 'I honest to God never meant to upset you. After all, you're still my baby sister.'

I swallow the lump in my throat. I've been mainly thinking about myself until now, but the more I think about it, the more I realise how awful it must have been for Anna, and that makes me even angrier with my parents, especially my mum because I've asked her countless times about my history. I keep thinking, every single time I asked her what she knew about my birth family, she must have thought about Anna. Or maybe she didn't; maybe she lied to herself as well as me, told herself I was an only child, tragically orphaned and in need of a home. I almost hope she did; it feels slightly easier to cope with than thinking about her – and my dad – walking away from that house with me, and leaving my eight-year-old sister behind.

CHAPTER THIRTY-TWO

Anna

You looked awful when I came round to talk about it. I said you looked like you hadn't been sleeping well, and you said you'd been awake all night the day I told you, and that you had nightmares the next night. I know it sounds horrible, but I was glad. You said it was the first time you'd ever had a completely sleepless night. Well, now you know what it's like.

I'm not saying your adoptive parents handled it well, they obviously didn't. They should have told you more, but when you think about it, by *not* knowing what happened before now, you've been spared a lot. I've lived with the horror of it for over thirty years. You got through your whole childhood without memories that would keep you awake all night, memories that would come back in the form of nightmares whenever you dared to go to sleep. See, I didn't have that luxury. I was used to sleepless nights by the time I was nine years old.

It was uncomfortable, sitting there in your kitchen, neither of us saying anything. Bonnie made it easier, because every time I looked at her precious little face, she smiled at me. She loves me, you know. She loved me even before she knew I was her auntie. Not that she knows that yet, but we'll tell her, won't we, as soon as she can understand? We should start getting her to call me Auntie Anna as soon as possible. She got a bit fidgety when she'd finished her biscuit, bless her, and you put her down so she could go back to her toys. So it was just us again. We were both quiet at first, but then you started asking me questions, which was fair enough, I suppose. After a while, it felt like you were trying to catch me out, but I told you all I know, everything I could remember about our parents, the house we lived in, Nana and Grandad (he died before you were born) and our two hamsters, Tom and Jerry. Funny, I'd forgotten about them until I was telling you what I remembered about the bedroom we shared at home. They had a fancy two-storey cage in the corner of our room, and you used to have tantrums because you hadn't learned to be gentle yet, so you weren't allowed to take them out and play with them, whereas I was.

Then you wanted to know more about the time after the crash, about staying at Nana's the first couple of weeks, then going to Gillian and Mike's. Again I told you everything I could remember, right down to the *My Little Pony* wallpaper we had in our room at Gillian's. I talked and talked, no matter how painful it was; you didn't care, you just kept asking more and more questions. Then you brought up – again – the point about me not telling you who I was straightaway; you said I was telling lies. I don't think I ever told you an actual lie, except maybe saying my foster family was my real family. But speaking of lies, you're not entirely truthful either, are you? For example, you told me you didn't need me yesterday because you weren't going in to school, but I had a sneaking suspicion you weren't being completely honest, so I thought I'd check, and I revisited my little spot on the other side of your garden wall. It felt a bit nostalgic, being there again after all this time. It's quite overgrown now, though I still think of it as my spot. Anyway, what I discovered was, you weren't telling me the truth, Emily, were you? You *did* go to school. I saw you come home just after five thirty. You were dressed for school, carrying that big leather bag, and you had Bonnie with you, so you must have dropped her off at Gemma's and then picked her up on your way home. Silly, really, because I could've picked her up.

We sat at your kitchen table and talked for hours until in the end, you said you had a headache and you had to stop and get lunch for Bonnie anyway. I had a headache too. I don't know if it was down to the weather or the stress of the conversation. It was hot enough to make you sweat, but not sunny enough to sunbathe. And it felt claustrophobic, like you couldn't really breathe. A muggy, headachey sort of day. After a couple of hours of this conversation, of trying to remember things I didn't always want to remember, my head was pounding, but I didn't say anything. I knew it was important to you, so I was prepared to carry on, even though it was making me feel ill. I even offered to make Bonnie's lunch, but you wouldn't let me.

'Anyway,' you said once you'd settled her with her egg and beans, 'thanks for coming round.'

It felt like I was being dismissed, which was hurtful, to be honest. I stood up to go, then I asked you if you fancied a coffee on Monday. When you hesitated, I said, 'Okay, I'll see you on Tuesday as usual, then.' But you still didn't say anything. Then, looking anywhere but at me, you said, 'I'll text you, okay?' I know you were struggling to take it all in, but I felt like I was losing you all over again.

And I couldn't let that happen.

CHAPTER THIRTY-THREE

Emily

My mother looks subdued, and I notice she's not wearing any make-up, which is unusual for her. I'm slightly surprised that she's not out playing golf or bridge or something, given that it's Saturday, but when I called, she seemed quite keen for me to come round. Which is also a bit of a surprise, because after the way I shouted at her last time, I expected her to be in one of her sulks.

'I just want to try and understand,' I say, when we're both seated at the table with a coffee in front of us, 'why you chose to tell me I was adopted, but not tell me I had a sister.'

My mother looks at her coffee instead of at me, then she sighs heavily. 'Your father said from the start that you should know you were adopted. I didn't agree at first; I was sure you'd soon forget about your early life – my father died when I was four and I've no memory of him whatsoever. I thought it would be simpler for everyone. But your father convinced me. He said that apart from anything else, most adopted children find out one way or another, and then it's an awful shock. And with him being a doctor, he always thought about the medical side of things, too. He'd had patients who'd only discovered they were adopted when some hereditary disease presented itself, or when a family member needed an organ or tissue transplant and it came out that their closest family may not be the closest match.'

I do my best to keep my voice steady and even. 'You really thought it would have been okay to let me go through life believing you gave birth to me?'

She looks at me now. 'I'm being honest with you, Emily.'

'I'm trying not to judge,' I say quickly. 'I'm trying to understand.'

She nods, and goes back to studying her coffee. 'I suppose I thought . . .' she runs her thumb around the rim of the cup, 'I think I thought we'd be closer if you assumed I'd given birth to you.'

I almost let my mouth drop open. The idea that my mother has even considered the closeness or otherwise between us disconcerts me, and this time it's me who looks away.

'As for why we didn't tell you about your sister, well,' she brushes some invisible crumbs off the table, 'you'd settled with us relatively easily – I suppose we thought telling you something like that after you'd adapted so well would set you back.'

'So Daddy agreed? I mean, it wasn't just you who didn't want to tell me about Anna?'

She doesn't answer straightaway, then she says, 'We argued about it, but he went along with what I wanted in the end.'

'Okay.' I nod, absorbing this. 'But what I really don't understand is, even if you genuinely thought I'd forget about Anna, how could you think she'd forget about me? She was *eight*. An eight-year-old child who'd just lost both her parents.' I can hear the edge in my voice again, though I'm trying hard to stay calm. 'You took away her only living relative and left her to fend for herself.'

'No,' she shakes her head, 'it wasn't like that. She had a lovely foster family. We knew she was being well looked after, and—'

'Well looked after? I can't believe you're trying to justify this!' The rage is bubbling up again and I'm not sure I can stop it. 'You really thought she'd be fine because she was fed and clothed and had a roof over her head? So, what, you thought she'd just carry on going to school and eating her meals and playing with her toys and everything would be the same? You took away her sister, the only thing she had left to link her to her dead parents – *my* dead parents. Christ, Mum, seriously? I know you and Daddy never had any siblings, but did you really, truly not *get* what that would've been like for a newly bereaved, traumatised child?'

She has the grace to hang her head. 'No,' she says in a hoarse whisper. 'I know it's hard for you to believe. You're a teacher; you *know* about children. But I don't think either of us understood that at the time, not fully. You see, your father and I hadn't planned to have children, but when we'd been married a few years, I changed my mind. Your father agreed so readily it made me wonder if he'd actually wanted

269

children all along and was just saying he didn't to please me. But anyway, we agreed. Then of course more years went by and it didn't happen, so we decided to adopt. But you see, I only ever wanted one child, and I was certain we could give you a good life. But your sister, she was old enough to remember her life before. And of course, she remembered what had happened to her, to your parents. It ... it would have been too difficult to take on a child who'd been through all that.'

I open my mouth to speak but she puts her hand up to stop me. 'I know I shouldn't have thought of it that way, but that's what I thought. I wanted a baby, or at least a child who wasn't used to calling someone else *Mummy*. Selfish? Yes, I realise that now. But I'm being honest with you, Emily. I wanted a child, but I didn't think I'd be able to cope with two. I convinced myself that we'd be better parents if we only had one. I told myself that if we made it as easy for ourselves as possible, it would be better for you in the long run. And the honest truth is that no, we didn't really think about your sister.'

When I get home, Simon shouts *hello* from the sitting room. 'Just doing a few emails,' he says, shutting his laptop quickly as I walk into the room. I'm not quite sure why he feels the need to explain. It flashes through my mind that he might be looking at something he shouldn't. But Simon's not the sort of man to look at porn, so I'm sure it's not that. Maybe he thinks I'll be annoyed that he isn't playing with Bonnie, who's sitting in the middle of the rug, surrounded by a pile of DVDs that she's clearly been pulling off of their shelf while Simon's been distracted. She grins at me. 'Hi,' she says.

'Hi sweetheart,' I say, my heart lifting at the sight of her smiling face.

'How did it go?' Simon asks.

I give him a summarised version. 'It's odd, though,' I add. 'A lot of the stuff she was saying is horrible, really, and shows how selfish she is. Or *was*, at least. But the odd thing is, I feel better for having had that conversation, even though hearing what she had to say wasn't pleasant. The thing is, for the first time, I think she was genuinely being completely honest.'

CHAPTER THIRTY-FOUR

Anna

The idea came to me as I unplugged the telly the other night, causing the usual flash from the multipoint socket. I unplug everything except the fridge before I go to bed, because this place is a death trap. I think the electrics must have been done in the fifties. I don't complain, because the flat's cheap – most of the places round here would cost another hundred quid a month, but not many people are prepared to live in a dingy little flat above a kebab shop. The smell was unbearable, and I swear the grease from their cooking seemed to make its way up here somehow. It's closed down now, though, thank God. The bloke in the off-licence next door reckoned someone must've reported them to the public health department. Anyway, next thing I knew, the place was all boarded up and they were gone. The landlord, Dusty – the name's something to do with drugs, I think – is just glad he's got a tenant at all. The flat had been empty for over a year when I moved in, so he let me have it cheap. He'd charge me even less if I was prepared to sleep with him. I couldn't care less about sex – it isn't important; doesn't mean anything to me. But I'm not sinking that low.

I went through the kitchen first, checking every shelf, drawer and cupboard to make sure there was nothing there that I couldn't bear to lose. There were a few old instruction manuals I didn't need and recipes torn out of magazines, some of which I knew by heart, others I haven't even looked at. I stacked all the booklets and bits of paper together and propped them between the herb jars and bottles of oil on the shelf beside the cooker. I double-checked that the smoke alarm had no battery – I took it out a couple of months ago when the battery was dying and the bloody thing kept beeping. Then I moved around the rest of the flat, closing doors to minimise the damage. I didn't have much in the way of things with sentimental value. In fact, all I had really were the things I needed to live from day to day: clothes, my laptop, cooking stuff. It was all replaceable, and I'd had stuff nicked so often growing up that I didn't really have anything to miss as an adult. My phone was in my bag, and everything on my laptop was backed up, although as long as I kept the doors closed, it shouldn't spread anyway.

Back in the kitchen, I pulled the oldest, thinnest tea towel out of the drawer and tossed it onto the tiny area of worktop next to the cooker a few times. Out of five throws, it landed close enough to touch the gas ring twice. Usually I was extra careful to keep everything away from the cooker top – there was so little space in this kitchen, it was quite hard *not* to have things too close. I shared a flat with a girl once who was so messy that things were always catching fire because they were too close to the cooker. We must have chucked away four or five tea towels with burnt edges or scorch holes.

I took a few things out of the recycling box, then I took the half-full box back downstairs and put it out the back by the other bins. I stacked the empty envelopes, flyers, pizza leaflets and a flattened down Cheerios box in a neat pile on the worktop, as though ready to be taken down. The pile of paper was near the cooker, but not too close. I relit the gas under the saucepan of cooked rice, then I took one of the pizza leaflets and held it to the flame. It caught, but quickly burned out. Wrong sort of paper. So I took one the flyers instead. *Turn your old gold and silver jewellery into cash*, it said. As if anyone round here has 'old gold and silver jewellery'. I put the flyer to the flame first and it caught straightaway so I used it to light the Cheerio box. Then, using the kitchen tongs, I held the tea towel over the flame. I was surprised by how quickly it went up – faster than the paper. Then all I had to do was to hold the flaming tea towel to the shelf where I'd propped the old instruction books and in seconds, not only were they burning away merrily, but the peeling wallpaper had caught as well. I'd started a proper fire.

By the time I'd thrown the kitchen tongs back in the drawer, the flames were eating into the wood of the open shelves where I kept my cooking pans. I'd put those shelves up myself because apart from the base units, there was only one cupboard on the wall when I moved in, and it was so high up I couldn't reach the second shelf. Smoke was already filling the hallway as I dashed out of the kitchen, back into the lounge where I'd left the TV on. My story would be that I'd put the rice on and fallen asleep. I grabbed my bag and glanced around. I wished I could take a couple of the pictures I'd put up, and the cushions and throw I'd bought to make the place look more homely, but that would look suspicious. Maybe if I was fast enough, there wouldn't be too much damage to the rest of the flat. All I needed was for the kitchen to be unusable for a while.

I grabbed my phone from my bag as I ran back into the hall, surprised at how thick the smoke was already. I could taste it. It was searing up my nose and stinging the back of my throat. I should have grabbed a wet towel or something to put over my face. My heart was beating fast and I could see the flames, licking around the kitchen door frame. Remembering that it was easier to breathe nearer the ground, I dropped down onto all fours, but my eyes were stinging and my nose and throat were burning and I couldn't see where I was going. I tried to crawl along the hallway to the front door, and for a moment, I thought I must have made a mistake and crawled into the bedroom instead, because my tiny hallway suddenly seemed endless and I couldn't find the front door. I was holding my breath. This was all happening much quicker than I thought it would. My phone was still in my hand but I couldn't see the keypad, and anyway, I needed to get out of the flat right now. My lungs felt as if they were about to burst. I was going to have to take a breath, but if I took it too soon, the smoke would get me. After what felt like an hour but was probably only a few seconds, I realised my fingers were touching the front door. It took a huge effort to stand, but I managed to get myself up, then I pulled the door open and stumbled out, slamming it shut behind me. I half ran, half fell down the stairs, wrenched open the street door and hurled myself out into the sweet, smoke-free air. I was overtaken by a coughing fit as, with a shaking hand, I started to dial 999. I was coughing so much I wondered how I was going to be able to speak, but at that moment I realised the sirens I could hear in the distance were coming closer and then, thank God, a fire engine appeared at the end of the road. Someone must have seen the smoke and called them.

The firefighters swung into action immediately. There were hoses and ladders, and lots of shouting. 'Anyone else inside?' one of them shouted at me. I was still coughing and couldn't answer. He shouted louder. 'Is there anyone else in this building?'

I shook my head.

'What about downstairs?' he said. He looked angry, as though he thought I might be lying. 'Are you abso-lutely certain?'

'Yes,' I said, triggering another coughing fit. By this time, quite a crowd had gathered, and then there were more sirens. An ambulance swung around the corner, and before I knew what was happening, I found myself being ushered inside. The paramedics were talking to me but I was coughing too much to hear what they were saying as they fitted an oxygen mask over my face and put a foil blanket around me. It was dawning on me that I was probably lucky to have got out in time, given that the kitchen had gone up so much faster than I'd expected.

'Feeling a bit better, lovey?' the woman paramedic was saying.

I nodded, surprised to find myself feeling emotional because they were being so kind. After a while, they took the oxygen mask off. I was still coughing a bit, and my lungs felt like they were full of flames, but at least I could breathe. There were a couple of policemen on the scene now, and one of them was talking to the firefighter while the other was walking towards the open doors of the ambulance. I could feel my heart beating faster as he approached. I put the rice on, I fell asleep in front of the telly. That's all I had to say.

'How are we doing here, then?' he said, looking more at the paramedics than at me.

'She'll have a cough for a few days,' the paramedic said, 'and we're going to pop her along to A&E in a minute, get her looked over. But she's going to be fine.' She squeezed my shoulder. 'Aren't you, lovely?' She looked back at the policeman. 'She's had a bit of a shock. There's some smoke inhalation, but she managed to get herself out before there was too much damage.'

The policeman nodded, then he lent closer to me and I had this idea that he was going to ask why I had started the fire. But instead, he said, 'What's your name, love?'

'Anna,' I said.

'Okay, Anna, we'll need to ask you some questions at some point, but we won't bother you tonight. You need to get yourself checked out first. Fire officer says the fire's out now, but there's a fair bit of damage so obviously you can't go back into the building. Is there anywhere you can stay tonight? Family? Friends?'

'Yes,' I said. 'My sister lives in Greenwich, I'm sure I'll be able to stay with her.'

CHAPTER THIRTY-FIVE

Emily

Simon's out again. He said he'd be back by ten but somehow, I know he won't – it's almost that now. I point the remote at the TV and turn it off. Even though it's early, I start thinking about going up to bed. I'm shattered. School's always tiring at this time of year, even though I'm only working three days. The heat doesn't help. But I guess part of it is the emotional exhaustion that comes from the discovery, at the age of thirty-four, of who I actually am. I finish my wine and look at my phone. I'm tempted to message him, but there's no point really. He could say he was anywhere, with anyone, and I wouldn't know whether he was telling the truth. I can't even remember who he said he was meeting tonight. Was it Marcus, or did he say Ben? Maybe it was Ben. Something about exam marking. At the very back of my mind is the ever-present fear that he's meeting Sarah. Cool, calm, uncomplicated Sarah, who knows who she is, and who can talk about something other than the discovery of a long-lost sister and all that comes with it.

I'm tempted to have another glass of wine before I go to bed, but I'm so tired, I decide to go straight up. As I stand, I catch sight of myself in the mirror above the fireplace. I don't look good. My skin is pale apart from the dark circles under my eyes, and my hair sits lankly close to my scalp, even though I washed it this morning. If I were Simon, I'd rather hang out with Sarah. Or almost anyone else, come to that. I allow a big yawn to overtake me. 'Do what you want, Simon,' I mutter aloud. I'm too tired to care.

My phone rings as I'm taking my glass through to the kitchen. Mum. It's unusual for her to call me at all, never mind this late, and I'm suddenly acutely aware that she's over seventy now, and even though she's annoying and selfish and has lied to me for years, I don't want anything to happen to her. 'Hello?'

There's a pause. 'Darling, I . . .' She sounds breathless.

My heart rate goes up and I'm wide awake again, wondering if I'll need to call an ambulance. 'What is it? Are you all right?'

There's another shuddering breath and I realise that she's crying.

'Mum? What's wrong?'

'I want to apologise, Emily. For everything.' There's a muffled sound, which could be her blowing her nose. Then she says, 'Oh dear. It's late, isn't it?'

For a second, I think she's talking about her apology, then she says, 'I'm sorry, I've only just this second looked at the clock. You're probably getting ready for bed.'

'It's fine,' I say. 'What did you want to say?' My voice

sounds cold, and I feel guilty, but I can't seem to help it coming out that way.

'I've been thinking a lot since we talked this morning, and going back over things, and I just wanted to say,' she takes an audible breath, 'I should have told you about your sister. You're right. It was unforgivable to keep that from you. I think I always knew it really.'

She's trying. I make a conscious effort to soften my voice. 'Then why *did* you?'

She doesn't answer for a moment, then, 'Deep down, I knew it was wrong. I knew I'd done a terrible thing in separating the two of you, but at the time I convinced myself it was the right thing for you as well as for me. I'm fairly sure your father would have taken you both, but I told him I would be the one doing the lion's share of the childcare, so it should be my decision. But I never did make a good job of it, did I? With you, I mean. I told him that if we just had you, I'd be able to devote everything to giving you the best start in life. But I can see now that I didn't do that at all. I made a complete and utter mess of it.'

I swallow. At first, I think she's waiting for me to say something, but then she continues, 'I discovered that although I wanted a child, I wasn't actually very maternal. My own mother wasn't, either – not that I'm using that as an excuse, but maybe ... Anyway, I found it difficult to ... to be close to you, to cuddle you and make a fuss of you as I should have done. And so quite naturally, of course, the consequence was that you didn't like me very much.'

'Mum, that's not—'

'No, darling, let me finish. I think you needed to protect yourself. I'd withdrawn from you. I deliberately didn't show you much affection because then you might be affectionate to me, and I wouldn't know how to return it. It was a ridiculous Catch-22, I can see that now. As you got older, I started to realise what a terrible mistake I'd made – not in adopting you, darling, I've never regretted that – but in pretending you'd never had a sister. The honest truth is, I don't think I could have coped with two of you, but that was no reason to behave as though she didn't exist.'

There's a long pause, and I'm trying to think of what to say, when she says, 'I don't have any right to ask you to forgive me for the way I've behaved in the past, but I will try to do better in future.'

I can feel tears threatening, and I have to swallow a couple of times before I'm able to speak. I've never heard my mother sound so vulnerable, so sad. 'Thank you,' I say. 'I think I understand a little better now.'

'I wonder . . . I'd like to apologise to Anna, too. Do you think maybe I should write her a letter? I'd like to meet her, but maybe I should write first?'

'Yes, I think that's a good idea.' Do I think it's a good idea? I don't know, but they'll have to meet at some point, so maybe a letter first would make that initial meeting less awkward.

It's gone ten thirty by the time I get off the phone to my mum, and I'm absolutely shattered, especially after that conversation. I'm not sure my mum and I will ever be properly close, but right now, I feel better about our relationship than I have in a long time. It sounds as though she really has been thinking about this and isn't just trying to pacify me. I do *want* us to be closer. Maybe this is something to build on.

I take my glass out to the kitchen, and then go round turning off all the lamps. I have my foot on the bottom stair when my phone rings again. My first thought is that it's my mum and she has more to say, but no, it's Anna. Why is she ringing me this late? I almost don't answer. I know it's a big deal for her, too, and she probably wants to talk, but I'm too tired. I consider sending a message but in the end, I answer. I'll suggest coffee tomorrow, maybe.

'I'm really sorry to call you so late,' Anna says. Her voice sounds odd, croaky. 'But I was wondering if you . . . I know it's a bit cheeky, but is there any chance you could pick me up from the hospital?'

'The hospital? What's happened?' I'm wide awake now. Something bad has happened. She doesn't sound like herself. 'Anna, are you all right?'

She starts to answer but is then overtaken by a coughing fit. Her voice, when it comes, is weak and hoarse. 'I'm . . . I think I'm all right. But there's been a fire. At my flat.'

'Oh my God! A fire? Are you all right? What happened?'

'I fell asleep. Left rice cooking on the hob. I don't really know how it happened.' She breaks off to cough again. 'They brought me here in an ambulance. They said there's no permanent damage, just smoke inhalation. They've given me

283

an inhaler to use but . . . I just . . . I can't go back to the flat tonight and I was wondering if, I know it's a cheek, but—'

'You can stay here. Of course you can. Look, one of us'll come and pick you up. Simon's out, but I'll call him now.'

'Oh, no, look, don't disturb him. I can always get a cab.'

'No, absolutely not. You stay where you are and I'll call you back in a couple of minutes.'

'Thanks, Emily. I really . . . Thank you.'

I call Simon three times before he answers. 'What is it?' he says when he finally picks up. 'Is everything all right?'

'Not really,' I say, and I hear the catch in his breath before I realise he probably thinks something is wrong with Bonnie. 'I mean, we're all okay here, but Anna . . . She's just called me from the hospital. There's been a fire at her flat. She's—'

'A fire? Oh God. She okay?'

'Yes, a bit of smoke inhalation, apparently. But she sounds awful, and the thing is, she can't go back to her flat tonight. Well, probably not for a few days at least, so I said she could stay here.'

'Sure,' he says. 'Of course.'

'She needs picking up. So I thought, either you could go, or you could come straight back and I could go.'

There's a pause. 'Can't she get a cab?'

'She offered to, but I said one of us would pick her up. I mean, she's just been in a bloody fire, after all. They took her to hospital by ambulance.'

'But I thought you said she was okay?'

'Simon, this is my *sister* for Christ's sake!' It's the first time

I've said it aloud. I'm still not sure if it feels any more real. 'And even if she wasn't my sister, she's done so much for us over the last few months, we could at least—'

'Okay, fair enough,' he says, and I'm sure I hear him sigh. 'I'll pick her up. I only had one pint when I got here. I've been drinking alcohol free, since then.'

It flashes through my mind to ask him who he's with because I really can't remember. But I don't. 'Okay then. Thanks. Where shall I tell her to wait?'

I seem to have got over my tiredness and while I wait for them to arrive, I busy myself making up a bed in the spare room for Anna. For my sister.

CHAPTER THIRTY-SIX

Emily

It's weird having Anna staying in the spare room. She's only been here two days, although it seems longer. I don't mean that in a nasty way. In fact, it feels more like it did when we first met, as though I've known her for years. Which is ironic, really. I'm doing my best to look after her. She insists she's feeling okay, but she obviously isn't. Her voice is still hoarse and I can see her wincing every time she coughs, so it's clear her chest is still hurting. I bully her gently to do the breathing exercises they gave her at the hospital and I'm trying to make sure she gets as much rest as possible.

On Monday morning, she's up before either of us, and by the time I go downstairs, she's already dressed, the clothes she washed last night having dried quickly in the heat – I've lent her some pyjamas, but obviously they're too big for her, and a bit warm for this weather, too. Bonnie's in her highchair, doing her best to catch wobbly bits of scrambled egg on her spoon; Anna is cutting toast into soldiers.

'Thanks for sorting her out, Anna, but honestly, she's quite happy to wait until we get up. You need to rest.'

'Oh, it's no trouble. I slept well and I'm feeling a lot better this morning.'

'That's good. You do sound a bit more normal.'

She smiles. 'Bit croaky when I first woke up, but it's fine now. Coffee?'

'Please.'

She takes a mug out of the cupboard with one hand while she slips a pod into the coffee machine with the other. It's as though she's been living here for ages.

'I was wondering, if you're not too busy this morning, would you be able to drop me back at the flat? I need to pick my car up apart from anything else, but I want to go in, see how bad the damage is. Maybe pick up some clothes.'

'Of course. Whenever you want.'

Anna and I have talked a lot more over the weekend, and I'm beginning to feel a bit better about it all. The more I think about it, the more I can see that she's been playing the Big Sister role without me even realising it. Right from the start she's done more than I've been paying her for, so it's good to have the chance to do something for her.

'Brilliant,' she says. 'Thank you. They said the fire didn't spread much beyond the kitchen, so hopefully most of my stuff should be okay.'

She puts my coffee in front of me and grabs a baby wipe to clean Bonnie's face. 'There, all nice and clean, my darling,' she says. 'Would you like to get down now?'

Bonnie nods, raising her arms to be lifted out of her highchair.

'Would you like me to come in with you? To the flat, I mean? I don't want to intrude or anything, but I thought maybe you could do with some moral support?'

'That would be brilliant,' she says. 'If you really don't mind? Although . . .' She looks at Bonnie.

'Yes, probably best not to take her with us. I'll get my mum to have her for a couple of hours. It's the least she can do.'

It's only once we're on the way to my mum's that I realise this could be awkward. Thinking back over the last few months, it dawns on me that whenever my mum was coming over – not very often, it's true – Anna would make an excuse to leave early. I thought she was just shy when it came to meeting new people.

'Anna,' I begin, and it's as though she's read my mind because at the same time as I start to speak, she says, 'I'll stay in the car when we get to your mum's.'

I don't answer straightaway. 'Okay,' I say after a bit. 'But—'

'You'll only be a few minutes, won't you?'

'Yes. I suppose it's better to wait until we have a bit more time.'

But when we arrive, my mum is looking anxiously out of the window. She comes out to the car as I'm getting Bonnie out of her car seat.

'Anna,' she says as she takes Bonnie from my arms, 'I know I owe you an apology, and I know it probably isn't good enough, but, well, anyway . . .' She hands Anna a letter in a sealed envelope. 'I hope . . .' but then she just sort of trails off.

Anna murmurs something I don't quite catch and slips the letter into her bag.

As we're driving to Anna's flat, it occurs to me that I've never seen where she lives.

'Left here,' she says, 'then left again. There,' she points, 'on the corner. The boarded-up kebab shop.'

I pull up behind Anna's Skoda, and as soon as we leave the cool haven of the air-conditioned car, we're instantly enveloped by the heat, which seems to be even more intense now than when we dropped Bonnie off less that twenty minutes ago. The front door at the side of the shop is already open and I follow Anna inside. The acrid smell is overpowering. It's an oily, woodsmoke stench that catches in the back of your throat. There are men's voices coming from upstairs.

'That's Dusty,' Anna says as I follow her up. 'Hello?' she calls up into the flat.

Two men look up as we step across the threshold into the soot-blackened hallway, the carpet squelching underfoot. Standing in what was once the kitchen are two men, one smartly dressed with a briefcase and clipboard, the other in his fifties, unshaven and greasy-looking. He's wearing baggy corduroys and trainers with a Led Zeppelin T-shirt that's seen better days stretched over his beer belly. Anna's landlord. I recognise him from her description, and from the fact that he looks the very epitome of the dodgy landlord.

'Anna! Are you okay?' He takes a step towards her, looking

her up and down as if checking for scorch marks. He looks genuinely concerned. 'What a terrible thing to happen. But you *are* okay? You wasn't hurt or nothing?'

'No, I'm good. Bit of a cough from the smoke, but no real damage. I don't—'

'Thank God for that, at least,' he says, then he gestures towards the younger man, who's wearing a pale grey suit, his dark skin emphasising the gleaming white of his shirt. His shiny shoes in particular seem incongruous amid the piles of ash and blackened debris. 'This is Mr Johnson,' Dusty says. 'He's here to do a report for the insurance.'

We both nod and smile.

Anna turns towards me. 'This is ... This is my sister, Emily,' she says. 'Who I'm staying with. Emily, this is Dusty, my landlord.'

He acknowledges me with a nod, but then seems to change his mind and extends his hand as well. 'Pleased to meet you,' he says. 'It's Tony really,' he says. 'But they call me Dusty because I used to be on the bins, see.'

'Ah, I see.' That's not what Anna told me, but I guess he's not likely to advertise the fact that he's a drug dealer.

'Well, thank you for your time, Mr Webb,' the loss adjuster says. 'I think I have all I need for now, so I'll leave you in peace.' He switches off his Dictaphone and slips it into his briefcase. They talk a bit more as Dusty walks him down to the front door, their feet crunching on the debris. While they're downstairs, Anna and I look around the rest of the flat. The worst thing about it is the smell, which is really sticking in my throat now. The main damage is limited to the kitchen and hallway, although the carpet in the bedroom is still soggy and there are black streaks all over the walls and ceilings. Even in the other rooms, there's a greasy film of soot over everything. Anna takes a suitcase from under her bed, wipes the soot off and packs a few clothes, all of which stink of smoke, although they look okay. 'We can put this lot through the washing machine,' I say. 'Even if it takes a gallon of fabric conditioner, I'm sure we can get the smell out. And they'll dry in no time in this heat.'

As we come out of the room, Dusty's coming back in, carrying a large dehumidifier, which he plugs in, muttering, 'I was sure I'd put a new battery in that smoke alarm, but they say there wasn't one in there. If I'd of known ...' He shakes his head. 'Anyway, never mind. Thank God you got out safely. That's the main thing.'

'I don't really know what happened,' Anna says. 'I put some rice on the stove and then went and put the telly on. I must have dropped off. So stupid.'

Dusty sighs as he looks around at the smoke-streaked walls, the charred wood and piles of ash and charcoal. 'These things happen, love. Long as you're all right. The damage is mainly to the kitchen, anyway. The rest of it'll need cleaning, obviously, and if that doesn't do it, I'll have to repaint. The hall carpet's knackered anyway so I'm gonna rip that up, but I've got another dehumidifier so with the two of them going, I should be able to get the rest dried out.' He looks around again. 'To be honest, you might have done me a favour in the long run. Once the insurance pays out, I'll be able to sort the place out properly, maybe whack a nice new kitchen in. It won't be nothing fancy, but it'll be better than what you had.'

'Does that mean the rent'll go up?'

He doesn't look at her, just puts his hand on his hips and looks around. 'Maybe. But we'll talk about that later. In the meantime, I've got another place you could use while we're getting—'

'It's okay,' I hear myself saying. 'Anna can stay with me while the work's being done.'

'Really?' Anna turns to me, her smile lighting up her face. 'Emily, are you sure? That would be brilliant, thank you.'

CHAPTER THIRTY-SEVEN

Emily

It's another sweltering day, and as I walk across the school car park, my shoes stick to the melting tarmac. I can feel rivulets of sweat running down my neck, and my dress is sticking to my back. When I open the car door, it's like opening the door of an oven. The seat is so hot under my legs that I actually flinch, and I have to click the seatbelt in really quickly because the metal is burning my fingers.

Traffic is a nightmare, and by the time I get home, I'm desperate for a shower. The burglar alarm beeps as I let myself in, and as I punch in the number to stop it going off, I notice the pushchair's gone. I'm guessing they've popped round to the shops. Anna's insisted on looking after Bonnie full time while she's staying here; she says it's the least she can do. At first, I said there was no need – I've got her booked in with Gemma until the end of term. But as Anna pointed out, that's only next week, and it'd mean less of a rush in the mornings.

It's twenty past six, so Bonnie's usually eating her dinner

by now. As I undress for my shower, I idly wonder what they've gone out for.

Feeling cleaner and cooler in a cotton dress and flip-flops, I move around the house opening all the windows in a bid to get some air moving through the place, even if it's only warm air. Then I head through to the kitchen and pour a glass of Sauvignon Blanc. I unlock the back door and step outside, expecting to see towels on the sun lounger, the paddling pool full of Bonnie's toys and the hose curled across the scorched grass. They've had the hose out almost every day for the last couple of weeks – Bonnie loves it.

But the cover's still on the paddling pool and there's no hose, no towels. In fact, the garden looks unused. So where are they? I sit at the garden table for a minute and try to enjoy my wine, but I can't relax. Something doesn't feel right. Back in the kitchen, there's no sign of anyone having been here recently, and the only things in the dishwasher are the things we used at breakfast. I go to the front of the house and look out of the window. I can't see Anna's car. It's fine, I tell myself. They've just gone to the park. Though why would she take the car?

When I try to call her, it rings and rings. 'Anna,' I say when the voicemail kicks in. 'I'm home now, and I was thinking Bonnie ought to be having her dinner soon. Can you give me a call when you get this, please?'

I keep my phone in my hand as I pace around the house, trying to think where they might have gone. I'm aware again of the slightly uncomfortable feeling that Anna is too attached to Bonnie. I know she's Bonnie's auntie so of course she loves her, but I'm still getting my head round that. And sometimes it feels as if they're almost too close, as if I'm being pushed out.

It's only as I start to walk upstairs that I notice the brand-new bag of nappies I'd left on the bottom step ready to take up is gone. I don't know why this alarms me. Anna's probably taken them up. But when I go into Bonnie's room, I freeze. Not only are the nappies not on or under the changing table, but there are other things missing too. The pile of newly washed clothes I left on the chest of drawers this morning; the baby wipes, the toys she keeps in her cot – a grubby white teddy, that hideous rag doll she loves so much, and her battered old Mr Fox – are all missing. It's been so hot, we've been using a sheet instead of a duvet, so it's not as though the toys could be tangled up in the bedding, but even so, I take the sheet out and shake it. That's when I notice her Peppa Pig pyjamas are missing, too.

My heart is starting to hammer as I try to make sense of it. *She's stolen my baby.* But then I think, *don't be so stupid.* I'm trying not to panic as I walk along the hallway and open the door to the spare room. I don't know what I expect to see, having not been in here since Anna moved in. The bed is neatly made, and the only thing of Anna's on the dressing table is a hairbrush. No make-up, moisturiser, or perfume.

I'm not sure why I feel guilty for being in here because it's my house, after all. But I hesitate before opening the drawers. There are several T-shirts, a few cotton tops, all neatly folded;

the blue hoodie in case the weather turned cooler, two pairs of jeans, shorts, a couple of bras and a jumble of knickers. I'm fairly sure this is all she brought with her – I remember helping her to pack these things and how we had to put them through the washing machine three times to get rid of the stink of smoke. Yes, it was definitely only one suitcase ... Where's the suitcase? I look around, but it isn't anywhere obvious. Then I search. On top of the wardrobe, under the bed, even in the wardrobe, where I know it can't be because there's barely any room in that wardrobe – it's full of clothes Bonnie has grown out of, my maternity clothes, and things for the charity shop. Anna's suitcase isn't anywhere in this room. It's gone.

I feel sick, and even though the sun is burning through the window onto my bare arms, my hands are freezing and I'm shivering. I call Simon but it goes to voicemail. 'Bonnie's gone,' I blurt. 'Anna's taken her.' I can hear the panic in my voice. 'I don't know what to do, Simon, please come home. Call me when you get this.' I'm struggling to hold back the tears. I don't want to sound hysterical. 'Please hurry up. I need you here.' I end the call and am about to call the police when Simon calls back. 'Emily, what's happened? What's going on?' I can tell by his voice that he's taking me seriously, which is a relief in one way, because I was afraid he might not, but scary in another, because if he's taking me seriously, it means there's definitely reason to worry. 'She's *gone*.'

'Okay, look, try to calm down.' His voice is softer, but with an edge underneath that tells me he's trying to sound calm when he doesn't feel it, which worries me all the more. 'I'm sure there's a simple explanation. Tell me exactly what's happened.'

'I just got home and they're not here. I thought they'd gone to the shop, but her car's gone, and I've called her and there's no reply, and—'

'Whoa, hang on a sec. You've just got home and they're not there? Maybe they're at the park?'

'Not "just", I mean twenty minutes, half an hour ago. And they wouldn't use the car to go to the park, it's only five minutes' walk. And her stuff's gone, and—'

'What? What do you mean, her stuff's gone?'

'Bonnie's things – clothes, toys, nappies. And Anna's suitcase. That's gone, too.'

'What? Fuck.' There's a pause. 'Look, I'm not being funny, but is there any possibility you could have got this wrong?'

'No, no. They're not here, her toys—'

'You're sure? You couldn't have made a mistake?'

'No!' I shout down the phone. 'Simon, I know you think I'm paranoid, but this is *fucking* serious.' My voice breaks. 'Our daughter is missing, Anna isn't answering her phone, and—'

'All right, baby, I'm sorry. Okay, look, I'll try her as well, but if she doesn't answer, we'll call the police, okay? I'm on my way home now anyway. Try not to worry and I'll be with you in about twenty minutes, okay?'

He's waiting for me to answer but I can't speak because I'm trying not to cry.

'Emily? I'm on my way, okay?'

'Okay,' I sniff.

When he ends the call, I allow myself to sob. I know how much Anna loves Bonnie, so at least I'm sure she wouldn't hurt her. But what if I never see her again? *Stop it, stop it, stop it.* I'm overreacting. I go along to the bathroom to blow my nose and splash some water on my face, then I take a few deep breaths to try and compose myself. I can't stop trembling.

I'm halfway down the stairs when I hear a key in the door. Thank God. He must have been closer than he said. But the door opens and Anna comes in, smiling, face slightly reddened from the sun, carrying a sleeping, pyjamaed Bonnie. 'Shush,' she whispers, fingers to her lips. 'Nodded off in the car, just as I planned.' Then her expression changes. 'Emily, what on earth's the matter? Are you all right? What's happened?'

'I thought ... I thought ...' I shake my head. 'Where were you?'

'We ... Wait, you did get my message, didn't you?'

'What message? I mean, no, no I didn't.'

'Oh dear.' She's still whispering. 'Hang on while I put Madam here to bed, then I'll explain.'

'It's all right,' I go to take Bonnie from her, 'I'll put her to bed.' In the back of my mind, I register a mild irritation that she called Bonnie *Madam*. That's *my* pet name for her.

'Careful,' she says. 'Don't wake her up.'

I want to scream at her, *She's my child; don't tell me to be careful.* But I don't, of course, because I don't want to wake my sleeping daughter. 'Oh, sweetheart,' I whisper into her hair as I carry her upstairs, 'thank God you're safe.' I lay her gently in her cot. She shifts a little in her sleep, but doesn't wake. As I stand there looking at her, waiting until her breathing settles into an even pattern, I check my phone, going into text messages as well as WhatsApp, but there's no message from Anna. That's when I remember – shit! Simon was going to call the police! I call him back, walking out of the room as I wait for him to answer.

He launches straight in before I even get a chance to speak. 'Hey, look, I'm nearly home. Police are sending someone round. Should be within half an hour, so—'

'It's okay, she's back.'

'She's back? Is she all right? What happened?'

I swallow. 'I'm not sure. Anna said she sent a message, but she definitely didn't. Anyway, they're back, so—'

There's a long pause. 'Right. Well, thank God for that. But, what the fuck, Emily? I told the police our daughter had been abducted—'

'I know, I know, I'm sorry. I don't know what happened. Her clothes were gone, her toys—'

'I'd better call them back.' His voice is tight with anger. 'See you in a couple of minutes.'

Shit, shit, shit. As I walk back downstairs, I can hear Anna talking to someone, and then I see them, two police officers, a man and woman, standing just inside the door. Anna turns as I come down the stairs. 'You called the *police*?' she says.

The male police officer looks annoyed. 'So is there a missing child or not?'

Before I can answer, Simon's car crunches on the gravel outside and a second later, I hear the car door slam.

'No,' I say quickly. 'She's back. But—'

'I'm so sorry.' Simon appears in the open doorway. 'It appears my wife was mistaken.'

Anna is shaking her head. 'I can't believe you called the police.'

'But where *were* you?' I say. 'What was I supposed to think?'

'All right, all right,' the policewoman says. 'Let's not get agitated.' She sounds calm and in control, and even though I know they're probably furious with me for wasting police time, I find her presence reassuring. 'Maybe we should all go and sit down for a minute while we try to ascertain what's happened here.' She looks directly at me. 'Okay?'

'Yes, of course. Come through.'

We all sit at the kitchen table and I offer tea but no-one wants it.

'I need some water,' Anna says. 'Anyone else?'

Both police officers say yes, some water would be good. And before I can do anything, Anna is taking ice from the freezer and filling a jug from the tap.

'Right, then,' the male officer says, looking at me. 'So you're the child's mother?'

I nod. 'Yes.'

He turns to Anna. 'And you are?'

'I'm Bonnie's auntie.' She looks at me, her expression both hurt and angry. 'I'm Emily's sister. I look after my niece while my sister and brother-in-law are at work and I just ... I thought I'd take her to the seaside for the day, that's all.'

Simon's shaking his head. 'I'm so sorry about this,' he says. I'm not sure if he's apologising to the police again, or to Anna. He turns to me. 'What on earth made you think ...?'

'I ... I panicked. I came home and they were gone and I had no idea where they were. There was no note or anything and—'

'But I messaged you! I said we should be back by the time you get home, but if not, we won't be long after.'

'I didn't get it.' I take my phone out of my bag and look at it again. 'No.' I hold it out for them all to see. 'No WhatsApp, no text. I tried to call you but there was no answer. I left a message.'

'I was probably driving,' she says, rummaging in her bag and pulling out her phone. 'Sorry, I put my phone on silent so it wouldn't disturb Bonnie. I knew she'd drop off in the car on the way back, you see – that's why I got her ready for bed before we left Southend.'

Then, as she looks at her phone, she frowns. 'Oh God. Look.' She turns her phone towards me. 'It obviously didn't send.' Sure enough, there's a WhatsApp message: *I've packed up a picnic and I'm taking Bonnie to Southend for the day. Don't worry, I have plenty of sunblock and I'll make sure I keep her in the shade as much as possible. Should be back in time for dinner, but if not I'll give her something out.*

'There,' Simon turns to me, 'simple explanation.' He turns

to the police officers again. 'We've wasted your time, I'm afraid. My wife sometimes gets a bit—'

'Hang on a sec.' I can feel my anger rising. 'That explains part of it, but what about all the nappies and clothes that are missing?'

'Missing? What do you mean?' Anna says. 'I took some nappies with me, and a spare set of clothes, but—'

'There was a whole pack there this morning. And where's the pile of clothes that was on the chest of drawers?'

'I put them away,' Anna says, looking wounded. 'And I took the whole bag of nappies with me – it was easier just to throw it in the car than try and work out how many I was likely to need.'

'Oh. I see. Well . . .'

'Well,' the policewoman says, getting to her feet. 'All's well that ends well. We'll be getting on and leave you to the rest of your evening.'

'Where are her toys?'

'Sorry?' the policewoman says.

'Her toys. She keeps her favourite toys in her cot, and they're gone, all of them.'

Anna smiles. 'Oh dear, I completely forgot!' She stands and as she goes to the utility room, says over her shoulder, 'They were getting a bit manky, so I put them through the washing machine with some of her other toys.'

I hear her open the washing machine, then she comes back in the kitchen with the laundry basket, containing half a dozen or so of Bonnie's soft toys, all looking bright and fresh and newly washed. 'Sorry, I meant to peg them on the line before we left. I'm sorry you were worried, Emily, but remember, I did mention this the other day, and you seemed fine about it then.'

'No, you didn't,' I say. 'I certainly don't remember you saying you were taking her to Southend.'

'I probably just said *the seaside*.'

Simon's shaking his head. Everyone else is looking at me, the nutcase, the paranoid wife, getting it wrong again, seeing danger and malevolence where there is only kindness and support.

And then I remember the suitcase.

'What about your suitcase? That's gone too.'

Anna's still smiling. 'Oh dear, I can see why you got confused. I popped back to the flat to pick up my laptop and a few other bits and pieces – took my suitcase to put them in, that's all. I'd better get it out of the car.'

CHAPTER THIRTY-EIGHT

Emily

'Are you sure you don't mind?' I say as I get ready to leave. 'I can easily drop her off at Gemma's.'

'No, it's fine. Like I said before, I'm happy to look after her while I'm here. It's daft to take her to Gemma's if you don't have to.'

Simon has barely spoken to me since Wednesday's debacle, but Anna's been unbelievably good about it. I apologised, obviously, and although she was clearly upset at first, she came round quickly. 'You're bound to be all over the place,' she said, 'especially when you think about what's happened in the last couple of weeks – me telling you who I am, then talking about what happened to our parents and that. It's not surprising you're going a bit loopy. Anyone would. But you've got to remember, Emily. I'm your *sister*, and I want the best for you. You've been so amazing, letting me stay here – I just want to do my bit, help out where I can. That's why I thought I'd take Bonnie out for the day.' Then she apologised again for the mix-up. 'I should have left a note as well as messaging you.'

Everything she says makes sense, and I know I probably overreacted when I couldn't get hold of her on Wednesday, but I still have this niggling feeling that things aren't quite what they seem. I know it's stupid, but if we were teenagers, I'd say she'd deliberately set me up to get me in trouble. But I suppose *thinking* she'd set me up is almost as childish as her actually doing it, and would she really be that childish?

I finish my coffee, say my goodbyes and set off for school. I wouldn't normally be in on a Monday, but we've all been roped in to help with Sports Day, and there are only two more days of school anyway, so I don't really mind. There's lots of fun stuff going on during the last couple of weeks of school, and the atmosphere is one of muted celebration – muted because we're all knackered, and celebration because the holidays are now so near that both kids and teachers can see the light at the end of the tunnel.

This year, I'm in charge of the hundred-metre sprint, the relay race, the tug of war and the teachers' races. Before I got pregnant, I was always up for the teachers' race myself – it was good fun and it was nice to hear the kids cheering me on. I might even have done it this time if it wasn't so hot and I could have got away with jogging bottoms and a baggy T-shirt. But it'll be shorts and vest tops today, and there's no way I'm putting myself through that.

We've spent the last couple of weeks reminding kids that,

while we encourage a little healthy competition, Sports Day is meant to be fun. Most of them are okay with that, though there are a few tears from a couple of Year 7s and one accusation of cheating in Year 9. On the whole, it's all fairly good-natured and there haven't been any injuries apart from a mildly sprained ankle in the long jump and a few grazed knees in the tug of war. All that's left now are the teachers' races. Quite a few of the kids who'd wandered off earlier are coming back now. They all love this bit. There are seven in the male teachers' race this year, including Simon, which is a bit of a surprise. 'I didn't know you were taking part,' I say as he lines up with the others. He's changed into trainers, I notice.

'Well, you've got to show willing, haven't you?'

I wonder briefly if he's making a point about me not joining in this time.

'It's only a bit of a laugh,' he continues, but then does a couple of elaborate stretches, which I'm not sure are strictly necessary for the hundred-metre dash. I'm pretty sure he's trying to impress Sarah, who's standing close by, waiting with Rachel and a few others for the next race.

I walk to my place on the starting line and lift my whistle ready to start the race. 'Ready,' I shout. 'Get set, and . . .' Simon, Rob and Sean all set off a fraction of a second before I blow the whistle, but despite their efforts, David, the chemistry teacher who, to the delight of the kids, is wearing a fluorescent green tutu over baggy grey shorts, black socks of different lengths and sparkly silver trainers, is the clear winner. Simon comes second, though, and looks reasonably pleased with himself.

Then it's the turn of the female teachers. A good turnout of fourteen, including Sarah, who as usual is looking tanned and super-fit in a pink striped T-shirt dress and trainers. I know it's ungenerous of me, but I really, really don't want her to win. Next to her is Rachel, who's wearing white shorts and a vest that's almost the same colour as her pale blonde hair. Like Sarah, she's slim and looks incredibly fit. Looking at the line-up, I'd say there are only two or maybe three others who are possibly fit enough to win, not least of these is Miss Sanchez – Juana. She's the newest of the supply teachers who've joined us recently. Teachers drop like flies at this time of year – immune systems, weakened by exhaustion, struggle to fight off summer colds and stomach bugs, and of course quite a few staff go off with stress. I do a double-take as Juana walks up to the start line. With her olive skin and long, coal-black hair, she always looks striking, but even more so today in a red crop top that sets off her hair and red-and-white leggings that emphasise her perfect figure. There's not an ounce of fat on her frame. Her hair is tied back in a ponytail that swishes from side to side as she walks. As I get ready to start the race, I notice there are more Year 9 and 10 boys gathering to watch this one, and I'm fairly sure Juana is the main attraction. I glance over at Simon, and I can't tell whether he's looking at Juana, Sarah or Rachel, but he couldn't be more obvious if his tongue was actually hanging out.

'Ready,' I shout, 'get set, and—' I blow the whistle.

As they set off, I feel momentarily envious of the enthusiastic support they're getting from the kids, some of whom are calling the teachers' names, but there are many shouts of 'Come on, Miss!' with no indication as to which 'Miss' they're supporting. From here, I can't see clearly who's in the lead, but my eyes are drawn to Sarah, who runs like a gazelle, long, tanned legs, covering the distance with no apparent effort. Rachel makes a good start but her legs aren't as long and she soon falls behind. Juana runs efficiently, the movement of her arms seeming to propel her forward as her muscular legs pound their way along the track.

According to Pauline, who's stationed at the finish line, it's too close to call between Sarah and Juana, so she declares it a tie. Tracey, who teaches geography and history and is considerably older than the winners, comes a surprise close second.

With all the events now over, all that remains is the presentation of the medals and trophies. The loudspeaker crackles into life and Ben's voice urges us all to make our way to the upper field for the prize-giving.

'Thank God that's over for another year,' Pauline says as we join the exodus.

'Yeah,' I agree. 'I'm not sure which is worse, this heat or the rain we usually have.'

Pauline says she prefers the rain, and shows me her sun-reddened arms by way of explanation. As I'm commiserating, I notice Simon, a few metres ahead, walking between Rachel and Juana. There's a bit of a bottleneck as everyone tries to funnel through the gate into the top field, and as they both move slightly in front of Simon to go through, I see his hand rest briefly on Rachel's lower back, then on Juana's. I can't see Sarah, but maybe she's gone on ahead.

CHAPTER THIRTY-NINE

Emily

The last day of term is always quite a nice day. There are no lessons, just a bit of tidying up in the morning and then after lunch, the end of term show, 'Woodview's Got Talent'. The kids have worked really hard for this, and some of the performances bring a tear to my eye. From time to time, I glance over at Simon to share the moment, but he looks fed up. I'm not sure he's even watching the show. He gets up and leaves the hall as soon as it's over, which makes me wonder if something's happened. I look for him after I've said goodbye to the kids, but apparently he's left already.

When I get home, he's in the kitchen. 'You're home early.' I try to sound bright. 'Where's Bonnie?'

'Sainsbury's. I asked Anna to pop round and get some ice-cream and she took Bonnie with her.' He sounds agitated and he's not meeting my eye.

'Oh, right.' I wait to see if he's going to say anything else, but he doesn't. 'What's up? Something wrong?'

He looks up at me briefly. 'I need to talk to you,' he says. 'I've asked Anna to babysit tonight. I thought we could get a pizza or something, maybe go for a walk. It's difficult to have a private conversation with Anna here.'

'Yes, I know, but it's—'

'I'm not saying it's a problem, I just need to talk to you, that's all.'

'What do you want to talk about that's so private?'

'No, I'd rather wait until we're out. They'll be back any minute.'

I shrug. 'Suit yourself.' I realise I sound a bit spiky, but he's making such a big deal of it. I know he finds it difficult with Anna being here – and it's not that easy for me, either – but she *is* my sister, after all, so I owe her this much.

There's a heavy silence, broken a minute or so later by the sound of the front door opening, and then Anna's voice chatting away to Bonnie as she gets her out of her pushchair. Seconds later. Bonnie toddles in, does a double-take when she sees me and breaks into a grin. 'Hi,' she says. Then she puts one of her chubby little hands on each of my knees, widens her eyes and says in a stage whisper, 'I-keem!'

'That's right, sweetheart. Clever girl.' I smile as I catch Simon's eye. He's smiling, too.

'Come on then, chick.' Anna lifts Bonnie into her high-chair. 'Let's get you some ice-cream.'

Simon barely speaks as we walk up to the high street, although we talk briefly about the bits and pieces we need to get done for school before we can really relax into the holiday. 'So,' I say. 'Pizza Express? Or . . .'

'You know what? I'm not all that hungry. Do you mind if we just go for a drink instead?'

'Fine,' I say. 'Trafalgar?' That's where we always used to go before we had Bonnie. If you get a window seat you can look out across the river, and it's a lovely walk along the Thames path on the way back.

'No,' he says. 'Let's go to the Gypsy Moth instead. I don't fancy walking very far.'

'But I thought you said . . . oh, never mind. Whatever.'

He goes in first, holding the door open for me, and heads straight for a table at the back of the pub where it's quieter.

'Large Sauvignon Blanc?'

I nod, and he makes his way to the bar.

In no time, he's back, but instead of a glass of wine for me and a beer for him, he's carrying a bottle of Sauvignon Blanc and two glasses. Something weird's going on, and I'm starting to feel uncomfortable.

I say nothing as he pours us both a large measure.

'There's no easy way to say this, Em.' He places the bottle carefully in the centre of a beer mat. Then he makes a sort of groaning sound and drops his head into his hands. For a second, he looks as if he might actually be crying.

'Simon . . .' I put my hand on his arm.

He straightens up, shaking his head. 'No,' he says. 'Don't be nice to me. I don't deserve it.'

'What are you talking about?'

'Emily, I'm so, so sorry. You don't deserve this, but I can't think of any way out. I've been racking my brains trying to think of a solution, but I can't.'

'Simon! For fuck's sake, what—'

'I – I didn't mean it to happen, Em, you've got to believe me. But I can't help how I feel. I – I've fallen in love with someone else.'

CHAPTER FORTY

Emily

When I wake up, it's a moment before I register that Simon isn't next to me, and then another blissful moment before I remember what happened last night. It all comes crashing back in – the memory of waiting innocently in the pub for him to come back from the bar, his agonised face, the tears in his eyes as he told me how sorry he was, and that he couldn't help it. Bastard! I feel my face crumple and tears start to leak from my already sore and swollen eyes. I don't have the energy to cry properly. In fact, I cried so much last night, I'm surprised I have any tears left. As I stand up, my hangover kicks in. I've not been drinking so much lately, not since I found out I have a sister. Or maybe it's the fact that the reve-lation brought everything to a head with my mum, but until last night, I haven't quite felt the need to anaesthetise myself with wine as much as I used to. But after Simon's bombshell, I just wanted oblivion. I down the glass of water I had the foresight to bring to bed with me, but I still feel desperately thirsty. Partly the wine, I guess, but I also feel like I've cried every drop of moisture out of my body. The strange thing is, on the one hand, I can't believe it – my husband of less than three years is leaving me for another woman. This happens in films and books, it happens to other people, not to me, not to *us*. But that, I realise, is why on the other hand, I *can* believe it. It does happen to other people, because it happened to Sarah, didn't it? Because I made it happen.

It's just gone seven thirty, so Bonnie must be awake by now. I open the bedroom door and immediately hear her voice from downstairs and then Anna's in response. Thank God for Anna. She was amazing last night, sitting up half the night with me, listening to me going on about Simon and passing me tissues – and glasses of wine. I need to get myself together before I click into mummy mode, so I text her instead of shouting down.

Morning! Are you ok with her while I have a quick shower?

She replies immediately. *Of course. Take as long as you like.* Then a second later, *I could take her out if you like?*

No, I reply. *It's fine. Be down in 10.*

A glance in the mirror confirms how hideous I look. My whole face is puffy and my eyes have virtually disappeared under their swollen, shiny lids. As I shower, I bite my lip hard in an attempt to distract myself from the thoughts that threaten to start me crying again. I don't want Bonnie to see me all blotchy-faced and pathetic. But she'll know something's wrong soon enough. My heart, already in tatters, starts to physically ache as I wonder how my baby girl is ever going to understand that her daddy doesn't live here anymore. I taste blood suddenly and know I've bitten too hard.

By the time I go downstairs, I look almost normal, apart from my eyes, which feel like golf balls. Bonnie's helping Anna put clothes into the washing machine, one sock at a time. 'Mama!' she says when she's sees me.

'Hey, baby.' I pick her up and hold her close for longer than usual. She cuddles me back, and the purity of her affection almost sets me off again, but I manage to get a grip.

'How are you feeling now?' Anna asks.

'Like shit.' I smile weakly as I put Bonnie back down.

Anna suggests we go to the park and then for coffee before going shopping for something *really lovely* for lunch. And for the rest of the morning, I'm blissfully distracted. It's only later, when Anna's putting Bonnie down for her nap that I start to think about Simon again. I didn't even ask him at first who he'd 'fallen in love' with, partly because I just assumed it was Sarah, but also because I kept thinking about that phrase – exactly the same phrase he used about me. Oh, I thought it was a wonderful thing to say back then, flattering and incredibly romantic. But now it sounds pathetic. 'Fallen', as though it's the result of tripping on a loose paving stone or slipping on the ice. You didn't fall, Simon. You leapt.

CHAPTER FORTY-ONE

Anna

It was quite a surprise when you apologised for your behaviour over me taking Bonnie to Southend last week, especially after I'd made you look like an idiot in front of Simon – and the police. I must have done an even better job of explaining everything than I'd thought. It's not nice, having someone you love taken away and not knowing where she is, is it? Realising her clothes and toys have gone, wondering if you'll ever see her again. But you only had to suffer for, what? An hour? I should have kept her out longer.

Anyway, you got over your hissy fit quickly enough, so you were happy for me to babysit while you and Simon went out for a drink. After I'd got Bonnie to bed, I made myself a coffee and went out to sit in the garden. I quite liked being out there on my own. I tried to imagine what it might be like if this was my house, and Bonnie was my child. I'd be a lot more grateful than you are, that's for sure.

After a while, I went back inside to find something to

eat – you said there was loads of stuff in the freezer and to help myself, but to be honest, I didn't fancy one of your posh ready meals. There are usually frozen pizzas, but not tonight, so I decided to order one. And it was when I was rummaging in my bag for my bank card that I found that letter from your mother. I'd completely forgotten about it. I took the scrunched-up envelope out of my bag and looked at it for a minute. Even the handwriting was posh. I wonder what she thinks will happen because she's gone to the trouble of writing a note? Silly cow. I didn't bother looking at it until after the pizza arrived. I don't really care what your adoptive mother thinks about anything, to be honest.

Dear Anna,

I wanted to write to you to tell you how truly and deeply sorry I am for my part in separating you and Emily when you were children. I won't go into lengthy explanations because I'm sure Emily will have already discussed this with you – I gather you are quite close friends, and I'm extremely pleased to hear that. But I wanted you to know that I now understand what a profound impact the separation must have had on both your lives, something I failed to fully grasp before now. I would give anything to be able to change the past, but as that is impossible, I can only offer my sincerest apologies.

I hope to be able to meet you soon, although of course I quite understand that you may not feel inclined to meet me. I would only ask that you give the matter some thought and

let me know, either directly, or via Emily, if you would be
prepared to see me, alone or with Emily, whichever would
feel more comfortable. I'm happy to go along with whatever
you suggest.

    With my sincere best wishes,
    Yours truly,
    Diana Mason

I screw up the letter and toss it in the bin. God, I hope she's
not going to try and be friends with me. Or worse, 'mother'
me. I don't really want to meet her, but I reckon I'll have to
at some point. You seem to be keener on her now than you
were when you first talked about her. I suppose I'm mildly
interested, but I'm in no hurry.

You came home earlier than expected from your evening
out, and you were a complete mess, practically falling into
my arms when I came out of the lounge to see what was the
matter. I'd looked out of the window when I heard raised
voices, and I saw Simon's car pulling away. Then I heard you
sobbing out loud as you opened the front door. 'What is it?'
I said. 'What's the matter?'

But you just shook your head because you couldn't stop
crying. It sounded as if you were hiccuping at the same time
and it seemed like you couldn't breathe properly. I'm not
really comfortable cuddling adults, but I did my best. 'It's
okay,' I said. 'Try and tell me what's happened.'

'Tell you ... in a ... minute,' you managed to get out
between sobs. I led you into the lounge and got you settled

on the sofa while I found a box of tissues. 'Th ... thanks, Anna,' you said, and for a moment, looking at your swollen, reddened face, it was like you were a little girl again, and I genuinely wanted you to feel better.

'I'll get you a drink,' I muttered, and I went to get the wine from the fridge. I poured you a large one, and took a small one for myself. You blew your nose a couple of times, then gave a big shuddering sigh, reminding me of Bonnie when she's had one of her tantrums. Finally, you managed to control yourself enough to take a few gulps of wine.

'He's leaving me,' you said.

'What?'

'Simon. He says he's in love with someone else, he couldn't help himself and he has to be with her. So he's leaving. I mean, he's left. He said he'll be back in a few days for his things.' Then you started sobbing all over again.

I pretended to be shocked, but of course, I wasn't. I knew pretty soon after I met him that he'd do something like this. I mean, bloody hell, Emily, are you really surprised? Did you honestly think that a man who would dump his fiancée – his *fiancée* – for you, wouldn't be on the prowl again when the shine wore off? *Couldn't help himself*, my arse. If he's done it once, he'll do it again – surely you knew that?

'Who is it?' I said. 'That Sarah woman?'

You shook your head. 'Rachel. Supply teacher.' You followed this with another little flurry of snot and tears. 'I've been so stupid. So *blind*. Maybe I'd have seen what was happening if I hadn't been so busy looking in the wrong direction. I wasted so much time and energy worrying that he'd go back to Sarah, it didn't even occur to me that he might move on to someone new.' You blew your nose again and refilled your wine glass. 'But *of course* it was going to be someone new.' I could hear the contempt in your voice. 'That's what I was, wasn't I? Someone new. The thrill and excitement of the unfamiliar.'

Well done, Emily – you've worked it out for yourself.

'So, he's gone to this woman's tonight, has he?' I said.

You nodded. 'Can't bear to be without her, apparently.' You got up and started pacing around the room, still drinking your wine. I was trying not to say too much. I'm used to keeping quiet in situations like this. I've always found that if you don't know how to behave, the best thing to do is watch and see what the other person does first. I know that with break-ups there's a point at which it's okay to start slagging off the ex, but I also know not to do that too soon. I tried to think of something to say because you'd gone quiet now and I felt like I should say something.

'I suppose it's a good thing that school's broken up, at least.'

'Is it?' you said, sitting back down and topping up your drink. 'Why?'

'Well, it's going to be difficult, isn't it? Working together when you go back?'

'Oh, he's thought of that. He's handed his notice in – he said it as though he wanted a fucking medal. He didn't want me to have to go through all that again, apparently. Made it look like he was doing it just for my sake. But I suspect the real reason is that he's realised that our colleagues might not be quite so forgiving this time. For one thing we're actually married, and for another thing—'

I finished for you. 'He's got a child.'

'Exactly!' You were on your feet again. 'The child that was so important to him it was the reason he left Sarah for me. And now he's leaving me and Bonnie. *Bastard!*' You pulled more tissues out of the box, but the tears were coming more slowly now and you were more in control.

I didn't say anything for a moment or two, then I said, 'I don't know how anyone can leave their child. I mean, how could anyone walk out on a little angel like Bonnie? I tell you one thing – he'll be sorry one day when he wants to see her again and she's forgotten who he is.'

You looked up at me quite sharply. 'He's not abandoning Bonnie,' you said. 'Well, I suppose he is, to a certain extent, but he'll see her regularly. We just need to sort out how it'll work.' And then you started sobbing again.

'So you're going to let him see her, even though he's treated you like a piece of shite on the bottom of his shoe?'

You looked shocked and I realised you've never heard me speak that way before. That twat of a husband of yours made me so angry, I let my guard down.

'Yes, of course,' you said after a moment. 'He's her dad.'

'But . . .' But then I thought I'd better shut up. I could see you didn't like what I was saying. Personally, if I was married to some cheating lowlife like him, I'd have had the locks changed by now and he wouldn't get within a mile of my child. But maybe you were thinking he might come back if you still had Bonnie in common. With a bit of luck, I'll put paid to that idea soon enough, but at that point I thought I'd better change the subject. 'Sorry, it just makes me really cross, seeing you treated like this. I wasn't thinking. But listen, Emily, you'll get through this. I'll do whatever I can to help. Cooking, shopping, looking after Bonnie – just tell me what needs doing, and I'll do it.'

You gave what I suppose could be described as a brave smile, seeing as how your face was still all red and blotchy from crying.

'Thank you, Anna,' you said. 'Sometimes, I don't know what I'd do without you.'

'You don't have to,' I said. 'I'm your sister, I'm here for you for as long as you want me.' You were sitting next to me on the sofa again now, so I thought perhaps I should have another try at putting an arm around your shoulder. 'We'll be fine without him,' I said, giving you a little squeeze. 'Don't you worry.'

CHAPTER FORTY-TWO

Emily

As I kiss Bonnie goodbye, Simon nods in the direction of the sitting room and says quietly, 'She's still here, then?'

'Yep. I've said she can stay until her flat's ready.'

'But it's ready, isn't it? I drove past there about a week ago – Rachel's cousin lives in the next road – saw the kitchen fitters loading up. It looked to me like they'd finished the job, but even if they hadn't then, they will have done by now.'

I find myself bristling. 'How can you possibly know that? And anyway, what's it to you whether she's here or not?'

He shrugs. 'Nothing, really. But think about it, Em. How long did it take to fit our kitchen? And from what you said, Anna's is about a quarter of the size.'

'She's my sister, Simon. She can stay as long as she wants.'

He shrugs again. 'Okay. Just saying. Anyway, see you later.'

But as I close the front door, I make a mental note to ask Anna how the new kitchen is coming along. It's been fantastic having her here these last few weeks, but I'm starting to feel like I need some headspace to deal with all this.

I watch out of the window as Simon straps Bonnie into her car seat. Rachel's sitting in the front, although why he can't leave her behind when he comes to collect Bonnie, I don't know. At least he didn't bring her to the door with him this time. Did he really think I'd be happy to have her in my house? Maybe that'll change. I suppose I'll have to speak to her at some point if they're going to stay together. I don't want us to be like my parents were at our wedding. In the photos, Simon's parents are holding hands, mine are standing three feet apart. But what's to say he won't get bored and move on to someone new again in a couple of years?

Rachel's turning round to talk to Bonnie. I can't see her face clearly, but I hope she's nice to my daughter. I wonder if she feels ashamed? She bloody well should do. She should feel at least as bad as I did. In fact, she should feel worse. After all, she knew Simon was married, she knew I was his wife, and she knew we had a child. 'Bitch.' I don't even realise I've said it out loud until Anna appears next to me at the window. 'Yeah, and *he*'s a cheating bastard. Come on, let's have a coffee.'

They're going to the zoo today, apparently. On Tuesday, they went to the seaside. Brighton. Simon seems to be relishing his role as part-time dad – Dad Who Does Nice Things. It's just over four weeks since he left, and even Bonnie seems to have settled into the new routine, but I'm still reeling. I'm not sure how much of it is the shock of him leaving me when I thought it was going to be happy ever after for us, and how much of it is because I feel stupid for believing that in the first place. We've still got to sort all the official stuff out at some point. I've cancelled the holiday we'd booked for the end of August, but apart from closing our joint account we haven't formalised any financial arrangements yet. Simon has already set up a fairly generous direct debit for child maintenance so I don't think there's likely to be a problem on that score. He's starting at a new school in September, in Kent, this time, and I'm guessing Rachel will be doing her supply work somewhere else. I'm not looking forward to going back to Woodview, though. Sarah will have heard, I'm sure, and she'll have every right to be smug.

'There you go,' Anna says, putting two mugs of coffee on the coffee table. 'What do you fancy doing today?' She's in a good mood. She seems to be making the effort to be cheerful in the hope that it'll rub off on me, but I'm not really feeling it.

I shrug. 'I'd better do an online shop, I suppose.'

'Come on. Let's go out and do something nice. You can't just sit here feeling miserable every time he takes her out. We could go for lunch. Have a look round the shops . . . Ooh, that reminds me. I bought you a present.'

'Oh, Anna, you don't need to—'

'It's nothing. It's only something I got cheap off of eBay. Hang on a minute.' She runs upstairs. She seems so animated lately. She's talking faster, even moving faster than she did before. Maybe I'm just feeling a bit fragile, but the sound of her running up the stairs annoys me.

She comes down carrying something in a taped-up black bin bag.

'What's this?'

'Just a little something I bought for the house. I thought they'd brighten up the lounge.'

She rips the bag open to reveal four lime green cushions, which she then arranges on the chairs and sofa, tucking them next to the cream cushions I already have. I'm a bit taken aback and I don't say anything for a moment, but Anna's looking at me, waiting for a response.

'Do you like them? I thought the colour was amazing. And it goes with the curtains.'

'Does it?'

'Yeah, look.' She grabs a bit of curtain and points out the tiny flecks of lime green running through the fabric.

'Ah. So it does.'

I'm really not sure about the lime green. It seems such an odd gift – surely a box of chocolates or a bottle of wine would be more normal? Frankly, either of those would be more welcome right now. Maybe I'm just in a shitty mood. I make an effort to smile. 'That's really kind of you, but you shouldn't be spending your money on—'

'Like I said, they were only cheap on eBay. And anyway, it's just a thank you to you for letting me stay. Although in a way, it's a good job I'm here really, isn't it? What with Simon buggering off. At least I can help you out with Bonnie and that.'

327

'I'm really grateful for everything you've done. Honestly, I don't know what I'd have done without you these last few weeks.'

She beams as I say this. And it's true, for the first week or so, I could barely make myself a cup of coffee, never mind deal with all the other stuff and be on the ball for Bonnie. Anna just quietly got on with looking after Bonnie, keeping the house ticking over and bringing me tea, coffee or wine, depending on the time of day. She's even made phone calls for me and fielded phone calls I haven't been ready to take. My mum offered to move in for a few weeks to help out, but even though things are a lot better between us, I wasn't sure I was ready for that. I do find myself thinking about it now, though. It's something I might consider when Anna's moved back to her flat.

'You've been brilliant, Anna. I'm going to miss you when you go home.'

Her eyes seem to darken briefly when I say this, but then she smiles. 'I don't think the flat'll be ready for ages. And anyway, you need me here.'

I hesitate. 'Is the new kitchen in yet?'

She doesn't look at me, but instead readjusts the position of one of the new cushions. 'No, I don't think so.'

I can't work out whether she sounds sad or sulky.

'No hurry,' I say. 'I was just wondering. Thing is, I know I've got to start coping on my own at some point.'

'Of course, but not yet. It's too soon,' she says in a rush. 'You can't possibly cope with all this and look after Bonnie properly as well. You're under a lot of stress. I was reading something that said marital break-up is one of the most stressful life events there are, and when you think that it came right on top of you finding out about me and what happened when we were little . . . Not to mention that big bust-up with your mum.'

'Well, it wasn't a bust-up really. The opposite, in fact – I think we're actually beginning to build a good relationship at last.'

She makes a sort of huffing noise.

'Anyway, you're right, it's a stressful time. But I think I need to start dealing with it.'

Anna stands up. 'Come on, little sister,' she says. 'You need cheering up. We're going out for lunch, and it's on me this time. To say thank you.'

When she asks me where I'd like to go, I choose the Italian place round the corner because there are tables outside, the food and wine are good, and it's not terribly expensive. I'm tempted by the comfort of lasagne, but end up choosing the seafood linguine because it's more summery. Anna has the same.

We're halfway down the second bottle of Valpolicella when I realise I'm quite pissed. I tend to forget that Anna doesn't match me glass for glass, so I always end up having more than I think I've had. 'I'd better slow down.' I look at my watch. 'He'll be back with Bonnie in a couple of hours.'

'Oh, don't worry about him. You'll be fine by then.' Anna refills my glass and tops up her own. 'Come on.' She raises her glass as if for a toast. 'Fuck him,' she says, clinking her glass against mine.

I don't think I've ever heard Anna say *fuck* before, and for some reason, it makes me laugh. I'm still giggling when the waitress comes to see if we'd like coffee.

'Tell you what,' Anna says, 'let's have a brandy coffee.'

'No, I'd better not, much as I'd like to.'

She's still looking at the menu. 'Better still, how about an espresso martini?'

I hesitate.

'Oh, come on,' she says. 'You *love* espresso martinis!'

'There is some truth in that.' I laugh.

The waitress catches my eye and smiles.

'Oh, go on then. You're a bad influence on me, big sister.'

When I wake up, it's almost dark. It takes a moment for me to reorientate myself, and then I remember I went out to lunch with Anna while Bonnie was with Simon. I leap up too quickly, causing my heart to pound and my head to spin. I peep round the door of Bonnie's room, and there she is, sound asleep in her cot, her Mr Fox tucked under her arm. Tears spring to my eyes as I realise I've done it again. It's been weeks since I've drunk this much – well, apart from the night Simon left. But this is just like that first time Anna and I had lunch together and I got stupidly drunk, and it feels all the worse because I've been doing so well lately.

Anna's in the kitchen when I go down, grating cheese.

'Ah,' she looks up, 'perfect timing. I thought I'd make you a cheese toastie – help to soak up the booze.'

'Thank you. How on earth did we end up having two espresso martinis? And how come I got pissed and you didn't?'

But as I say this, I remember that Anna hardly ever topped up her own glass, and even when she did, it was only by a couple of centimetres, so I probably had around a bottle and a half of wine. And come to think of it, she only took a few sips of the second martini before pushing it towards me and insisting I finish it.

Anna shrugs. 'I drink slower, I think. Anyway, we can't both get pissed, can we? Not when we've got Bonnie to look after.'

I feel a ripple of shame when she says this, and slight annoyance that she's pointed it out, although I'm sure she didn't mean to make me feel bad. She's right, though. I wasn't in a good state earlier. In fact, I remember having to hang onto her arm as we walked home because I was weaving all over the pavement, and she had to key in the numbers for the burglar alarm because I was seeing double. The last thing I remember is her helping me upstairs and taking my shoes off after I collapsed face down on the bed.

'Thanks for looking after me, Anna, but you shouldn't have to be responsible for me like this. Did you put Bonnie to bed?'

'That's what big sisters are for. Anyway, yes, I put Madam to bed. I didn't want *him* coming in, not with you ...' She chuckles. '*Indisposed*. I told him you had a migraine.'

I nod. 'Thank you. I'm sorry to put you in that position – again! You really shouldn't have to lie for me.'

'It's fine. I'm just glad I was here to help.'

I smile. 'You can't *keep* looking after me, getting me out of trouble. It's not your job. You do so much for us already – it must be getting in the way of your own life.'

Again, she reassures me that it's not a problem. But things really can't go on like this for much longer, and I'm wondering how much I subconsciously take advantage of her being here. At least if my mum was here, I wouldn't be going out and getting pissed at lunchtime. As we eat our toasted sandwiches, I raise the subject of her flat again. 'But listen, going back to what I was saying earlier, I was wondering if perhaps you could have a chat with your landlord? Just to see how everything's coming on, maybe get a rough idea of when the flat might be ready?'

Her face clouds over.

'Don't worry,' I say quickly, 'you can stay here as long as you need to, it's just that, you know I said my mum and I had been getting on a bit better? Well, she's offered to move in for a while, to help out with Bonnie and be supportive in general. I said no at first, but the more I think about it, the more I think it would be good for us. Bonnie doesn't really know her grandma as well as she should.'

'Her grandma's dead.'

The words drop like a stone. The way she says it sends a chill right through me. I've obviously upset her. 'Sorry, Anna. I didn't think.'

Now she's said it, it feels odd to me, too, knowing that Bonnie will never know her biological grandmother. But I should have thought about how it might affect Anna, given that she actually remembers our mother.

'Thing is,' I say after a moment, 'as far as Bonnie knows at the moment, my adoptive mum is her grandma. As soon as she's old enough to understand, I'll tell her about her birth family. In fact, maybe we can tell her together.'

Anna nods, then turns back to what she's doing. I make tea to have with the toasted sandwiches, which we eat while we watch some silly quiz show on TV. I feel much better afterwards. But Anna's good mood has disappeared. I only put the telly on to break the silence. She's obviously upset with me, and I'm getting the strong impression that she doesn't want to move out. I want to tell her that she's welcome to come and visit whenever she likes, but there's been such a heavy silence since I mentioned my mum moving in that it's hard to bring it up. I also want to tell her that I'm still happy to pay her for looking after Bonnie when I go back to school – she might be worried that I'll assume she'll do it for nothing because she's Bonnie's auntie. I'll have to find a way of bringing it up soon.

At about ten, Anna says, 'I reckon you're going to struggle to sleep tonight, after having that long nap this afternoon.'

'Yes, probably.' I smile, relieved that she's talking. Perhaps she wasn't sulking. Maybe I'm just being paranoid again.

'Tell you what, why don't I make us some cocoa? I know it's not really cocoa weather, but my foster mum used to make it for me when I couldn't sleep. There's something about proper cocoa rather than hot chocolate that really works.'

'No thanks,' I say. 'I don't fancy cocoa.'

'No, but I bet you don't fancy lying awake half the night either.'

'True. The doctor gave me some sleeping tablets, but I'm not supposed to take them if I've been drinking.'

'There you are then. Honestly, give it a go.' She stands up. 'I'm going to have some anyway. Tell you what, I'll make it, and if you don't fancy it, just don't drink it.'

She looks so eager to please, I don't want to hurt her feelings. 'Okay,' I say. 'Thank you. I'll give it a try.'

Ten minutes later, she comes back from the kitchen with two mugs of cocoa. 'There.' She puts mine on the coffee table in front of me. 'That should knock you out.'

CHAPTER FORTY-THREE

Emily

My mouth is dry, I'm drenched in sweat and I feel like I'm about to throw up. I've woken up disorientated before, but this is something else. My head feels thick and woolly, and – I know this sounds crazy – but when I first opened my eyes, I couldn't remember where I was, or even who I was. I feel detached, disconnected, disorientated; something very bad has happened but I can't remember what. I lie there, staring up at the ceiling and feeling absolutely terrified. Slowly, very, very slowly, I start to feel like myself again. I want to try and get out of bed, but I don't think I can move. Am I paralysed? Maybe I'm dying; or perhaps I'm already dead? Then little glimpses come back: Bonnie ... I can't die, because I have a baby daughter. And then I remember Simon, but ... he went off with Rachel. My mum. She loves me, after all. I feel sick. I'm going to be sick ... I try again to move and this time, I manage to drag myself out of bed, but my body is so heavy and my legs so leaden that all I can do is stumble towards the bathroom, only just making it in time.

It's only as I'm rinsing my mouth out that the rest of it starts to come back. Simon came to take Bonnie out, I got drunk at lunchtime, but then I slept in the afternoon, and when I woke up, I was okay, so why do I feel like this? I'm looking out of the window, but I can't work out what time of day it is. The light doesn't feel like morning light, but it's not dark, and I'm sure I went to bed early. Anna made me cocoa. At the thought of cocoa, another wave of nausea overtakes me and I retch a couple of times, but nothing comes up. I open the bathroom cabinet to look for something to settle my stomach, and as I reach inside, I knock a bubble pack into the basin. My sleeping tablets. I try to think back to last night. No, I definitely remember thinking I shouldn't take them having had all that booze at lunchtime. But . . . I look at the pack in my hand, trying and failing to remember how many were in there. I'm sure there were more than this.

After I've washed and dried my face, I glance in the mirror. I look hideous, with dark circles under my eyes, and hair sticking up all over the place. My watch is lying on the windowsill. It takes me a moment to make sure I have it the right way up. It looks like it says ten to three, but that can't be right. It doesn't get light until about six. Slowly, very, very slowly, it dawns on me that it is in fact ten to three in the afternoon.

'Anna?' I call as I go downstairs, struggling to move my still-sedated body. The house is eerily quiet. The kitchen is still and empty, the kettle stone cold. Bonnie's highchair is still at its place in the corner. 'Anna? Bonnie?' I check in the sitting room, then the garden. No sign of them anywhere. Bonnie's pushchair has gone. Stay calm, I tell myself. She's taken Bonnie out so as not to disturb me. Their breakfast things are still in the dishwasher, but nothing from lunch, which means they've been out for at least three hours. This is feeling uncomfortably like that day a few weeks ago when I panicked unnecessarily. Breathe, I tell myself. My sister has taken her niece out for the day so that I can get some rest, that's all. But given what happened last time, I would have expected Anna to leave a note. I look around for my phone, but I must have left it charging by the bed. I'm trying to move quickly, but I feel as if I am wading through treacle as I drag myself back up the stairs. My phone isn't by the bed, and it's taken such an effort to get up here, I feel like crying.

Bonnie's room is bathed in a warm, rose-coloured hue as the sun pushes through the still-closed pink curtains. I draw them back to let in more light and, just like before, Bonnie's toys are gone from her cot. This time, the duvet is gone, too. Panic now rising, I go into Anna's room and fling open the drawers. There are a few things still there, but there's no doubt this time. Most of her clothes are gone. For a few seconds, I'm frozen, paralysed, as I stare into the empty drawers, not wanting to believe what is patently obvious. I almost fall down the stairs, partly because I'm hurrying, and partly because my legs still won't work properly. My phone is still in the sitting room, but as I pick it up, it flashes a warning that I only have 8 per cent charge left, which means it's going to die any second. Why didn't I bring the charger down with me? Maybe there's one in the kitchen. Frantically, I check all the sockets in case I've left one plugged in, then I search through the drawers, finding one at last at the back of the cutlery drawer. I attach it to my phone and plug it into the slot in the socket, and soon as it's safely charging, I call Anna's number. *The mobile phone you are calling is switched off. Please try again later.*

Next, I call Simon. He won't want to be disturbed in his little love nest, but tough shit.

'Emily, what's up?' He sounds lazily relaxed, and I wonder if they're in bed.

'It's Bonnie, she's gone. Anna's taken her. Really, this time. I'm certain. Everything's gone, her toys, her duvet. And Anna's stuff, too.'

There's a pause, and then I hear him sigh. 'Emily, look, I'm sure there's a reasonable explanation.'

'I'm telling you, she's gone. I don't know whether Anna's trying to scare me, whether I've upset her ... I don't know what's going on, but please Simon, this isn't paranoia, I promise.'

He doesn't answer immediately. I can hear him talking sotto voce, probably explaining to Rachel that his loopy wife is imagining things again.

'Are you even listening?' I say when I hear him moving the phone closer to his ear again.

Another sigh. 'Yes, I'm listening. Tell me what happened, then.'

So I tell him again about everything being gone, but he interrupts. 'So hang on, if this was this morning, why have you only just—'

'It wasn't this morning. I've just found everything missing, just now.'

'But I thought you said it was when you got up.'

I swallow. 'I know it sounds weird, but I slept until ten to three. I think I must have taken a sleeping pill without realising it.'

'Emily, sleeping pills don't make you sleep for that long. Were you drinking last night? Tell me the truth.'

'Not last night, no, but I did have a couple of glasses of wine at lunchtime.' The words hang in the air. Simon doesn't answer and I get the strong impression that he knows I'm lying. 'Okay, no, it was more than a couple of glasses, and yes, I was drunk, but—'

'Oh, for fuck's sake, Emily!'

'No, listen, please. Yes, I got drunk, I slept in the afternoon, but then I was fine, Anna made me something to eat and then . . .' As I'm talking, I remember that bubble pack of sleeping pills falling out of the bathroom cabinet, the blinding headache and leaden limbs. 'I think Anna put sleeping pills in my cocoa.'

He laughs. I mean really laughs. 'Oh, Emily, seriously? You've been watching too much television. I know Anna's a bit strange, but come on.'

'I know it sounds mad, but I thought it was weird when she kept on about the bloody cocoa. Then, when I woke up, I had this terrible headache, like a hammer going in my brain, and—'

'It's called a hangover, Emily. Look, have you tried calling her?'

'Of course I have! What do you think I am, some sort of fucking idiot?'

'No,' he says, 'but I think you're being paranoid again. Now, I'm sure they'll turn up any minute, just like last time. Take some pills for your headache, have a bath, go for a walk or something, but for Christ's sake, calm down and be reasonable.' And he rings off.

'Bastard!' I rip the phone away from the charger and hurl it across the room, then retrieve it to try Anna again, but her phone's still switched off. I'm about to call the police, but after last time, they probably won't take me seriously either.

CHAPTER FORTY-FOUR

Emily

As soon as I'm on the phone to my mum, it all comes out in a rush and I can hear how jumbled it is, and how far-fetched it sounds when I say that I think Anna put sleeping tablets in my drink, but she listens without interrupting.

'All right, darling, try to calm down. It's quite a lot to take in. Now, first of all, when you say you think she's *taken* Bonnie, what do you mean? Is it possible she might have taken Bonnie out somewhere, to the park or something?'

'Yes, but why would she take her pyjamas and duvet?'

'And you're sure she's taken them? They're not in the laundry?'

'No, they're definitely missing.'

I haven't actually checked that, but I know I'm not going to find them in the laundry basket or the washing machine, not this time.

'I see,' she says. Then she asks more questions, all of them reasonable. I can tell she's sceptical, but also that she's trying hard not to be, and I'm grateful.

'Now, I'm not saying I don't believe you, but what makes you think she put something in your drink? And is it at all possible that you could have taken a sleeping pill, forgotten you took it and then accidentally taken another one?'

I tell her about the cocoa, how insistent Anna was, and how absolutely awful I felt when I woke up. 'It's beginning to wear off slightly now, but this definitely isn't normal. I've taken those tablets a few times since Simon left, and they certainly send me to sleep, but I still wake up at my normal time.'

Then she asks if I've called the police, and if I've told Simon, so I have to explain why I'm worried the police won't take me seriously. I tell her what happened last time and that as a result, Simon is completely convinced that I'm paranoid. 'I don't know what to do, Mum.'

'All right, darling. Try not to worry. I'll come over now and we'll work it out. Go and make yourself a cup of tea, and I'll be there as quickly as I can.'

'Thank you.' As soon as I end the call, I burst into tears. I can't ever remember feeling so grateful to my mother. For the first time, certainly in my adult life, I really want her here with me. While I'm waiting, I go into the utility room to check the washing machine and laundry basket, but there's no sign of Bonnie's stuff, as I knew there wouldn't be. I try Anna's phone again, but still nothing.

I do as I'm told and make a cup of tea, but all I can do is

stare at it. I start to pace up and down the kitchen, which usually helps me to think, but today it's hard to make my legs move. What I don't understand is why Anna's doing this. She surely can't be punishing me for asking when her flat might be ready? She did seem upset about that ... Suddenly, the idea that she may have taken Bonnie to the flat jumps into my head. Maybe she's just trying to scare me, and she'll look all innocently surprised. She'll say something like, *I thought it would be nice for her to see where I live. You were worried? Sorry, must have turned my phone off by accident.*

Yes, I decide. That's what's happened. Work on the flat must have finished after all, and she's taken Bonnie there. I start to look for my car keys and then realise that I shouldn't be driving while I feel like this, and also, I'm still in my pyjamas. Maybe a shower will wake me up. At least it'll pass a few minutes while I'm waiting for my mum.

I'm dressed and standing outside as she pulls up. 'Change of plan,' I say, getting into the car. 'I think she might have taken Bonnie to her flat. It's only a couple of miles away. I'll direct you.'

If I was worried that my mum wasn't taking me seriously, I needn't have been. As we drive to New Cross, she keeps glancing at me, and she pats my arm a couple of times. 'Try not to worry, darling. You're probably right. From what you've said, it sounds like it's the sort of thing Anna might do without really thinking.'

I used to hate the fact that my mum was always so calm and in control, but right now, I'm finding it incredibly

343

reassuring. She thinks we're going to find Bonnie with Anna at her flat, so maybe that is realistic. I try to block out the fact – and I'm becoming increasingly sure that it is a fact – that she deliberately drugged me last night, because why would she do that, just to play house with my daughter for a few hours?

'I meant to ask you,' Mum says. 'Did she read my note?'

'I don't know, to be honest. She hasn't mentioned it, and I haven't asked because I've been a bit preoccupied.'

'Oh darling.' She glances at me and pats my arm again. Then shakes her head. 'I still can't get over Simon behaving like this. Perhaps he just needs to get it out of his system.'

I make an involuntary sound that can only be described as a derisive snort. She doesn't say any more about Simon.

'Next left,' I say, 'then left again. It's just here, on the right.' We pull over and get out of the car. There's no sign of life, but I ring the bell anyway, glancing up and down to see if there are any vans that might belong to decorators or kitchen fitters, but there aren't. It looks like Simon may have been right. I ring the bell again and look through the letterbox, but I can't see anything.

'You've tried her phone again, I take it?'

I nod. 'I've been trying about every fifteen minutes.'

'Well, try it again now,' my mum says, 'and I'll put my ear to the letterbox to see if I can hear it ringing.'

I'm impressed. 'Good idea.'

She crouches down to listen at the letterbox while I call the number, but as soon as the recorded message kicks in, I remember. 'Shit, I forgot. It's turned off.' I step back on the pavement and look up at the flat, but there's nothing to see.

We get back in the car and are about to set off when a white van pulls up in front of us. When the door opens, I grab my mum's arm.

'Mum! That's her landlord!'

She turns the ignition off and we both get out again. 'Dusty?'

He turns and looks at us, but obviously doesn't recognise me.

'I'm ... I'm Anna's sister, I was here with her the other week, after the fire.'

'Ah, that's where I've seen you before. How are you, love? You all right?'

'I was wondering, have you seen Anna at all? I thought she might be at the flat.'

'Ain't seen hide nor hair of her, love. I must of left half a dozen messages at least, but not a dickybird. I was just going to check to see if she's back.'

'The work's all done then? The new kitchen and everything?'

'Been done and all ready for her for the last two weeks. I didn't hear from her but I thought she'd want to be back in as soon as possible, so I came round to check and ...' He shrugs. 'No sign of her.' He takes a big bunch of keys out of his pocket. 'You've rung the bell, then?'

'Yes, but there's no answer.'

'Well,' he jangles his keys, 'I don't like going into a

property when the tenant's not there, but she's not paid no rent since the fire, so I reckon I'm entitled. Just so I can see if she's been in, like.'

'We understand,' my mum says. 'Would you mind if we came up with you? We do need to speak to Anna quite urgently, so it would be good to know if she's been here recently.'

'Yeah, 'course you can, darlin'.' He leads the way back into the house through the main front door. I catch my mother's eye and she tries to smile, but I can see that she's worried now, too.

'It's not like Anna,' Dusty says as we follow him up the stairs. 'She's been a good tenant up until now. Always paid her rent on time, no trouble in all the time she's been here. Well,' he fitted his key in the lock, 'I suppose it's not that long, really.'

'How long has she lived here?' I ask. I've never really thought about this before.

'Eighteen months, I think, maybe a bit more.' He looks at me curiously. 'Had you not been in touch, then, you and her?'

'No, not until quite recently.'

He nods. 'Can't remember where she said she lived before, but I got the impression she moved around a lot.'

'Really?' my mum says. 'May I ask what gave you that impression?'

'Just that she didn't have much stuff when she moved in. I mean, not that she needed much – the place is let fully furnished, with telly, DVD player and all that. But you ladies

346

usually have at least half a dozen suitcases full of clothes, don't you? Plus one for your make-up.' He chuckles. 'But she came with one suitcase and a rucksack, if memory serves. Still, none of my business.'

The door to the flat swings open and the first thing I notice is the smell of fresh paint, so different to the acrid stench of smoke and burnt wood last time I was here. The hall carpet has been replaced, and I can see the new kitchen. Basic, but new and shiny. There are no signs of anyone having been here recently, and the plastic boxes containing Anna's pots, pans and crockery are still stacked up in the corner.

'Well,' Dusty says, dropping the big bunch of keys onto the work surface. 'Looks like she's been in anyway.'

'What?'

He nods towards a letter lying opened next to his keys. 'Thames Water. That'll be her water rates.'

I grab the envelope from him and check the date on the postmark. 'Look.' I pass it to my mum. 'This must have come in the last two days.'

'So you've not seen her, either?' Dusty says.

I don't want to give him too much detail, so I just say, 'No, not for a bit.'

'Well, if you speak to her before I do, will you tell her to call me. I need to know whether she still wants the place because I can't afford to have it sitting empty, like.'

'Of course,' I say. 'I'm sure she'll turn up.'

I wish I believed that.

'I'll give her one more week,' Dusty says, reaching for his

keys again. As he picks up the big bunch, there's a clatter as a key falls to the floor. He stoops to pick it up. 'Hang on a minute,' he says, holding the Yale key up by its yellow tab. 'This is her key. Must have been sitting there on the work-top.' He turns to me. 'Looks like she's done a runner.'

CHAPTER FORTY-FIVE

Emily

Once we're outside the flat, my mother calls Simon and tells him to meet us back home, her voice becoming progressively firmer and more irritated as the conversation continues. 'No, Simon,' I hear her saying, 'she is not being paranoid, and yes, I know about the false alarm a few weeks ago – Emily has explained.' Then it goes quiet for a moment. 'Yes, she's told me about that, too, and to be perfectly candid with you, Simon, it suggests to me that she's not been happy for some time, and as you're clearly aware that she was struggling, you could perhaps have offered some help and support instead of running off with another woman at the first opportunity.' She gives an exasperated sigh. 'Anyway, that's all I'm going to say on that matter. As for the matter in hand, Emily and I are on our way back from Anna's flat where the landlord has confirmed that she has, as he puts it, "done a runner", so will you kindly get your priorities right and meet us back at the house, preferably within the next twenty minutes? We'll need to give the police as much information as possible so they can find your missing daughter. Goodbye.'

At any other time, in any other situation, I would be feeling almost happy as I listened to my mum taking charge, sticking up for me, being supportive. But right now, all I can think of is Bonnie and where she might be.

As soon as my mum's off the phone with Simon, her air of calm efficiency slips a little and I can see how worried she is. Her hands are gripping the steering wheel and she's biting her lip as she drives, taking the corners too fast and then pulling out in front of a motorbike, which only just manages to swerve out of her way. The rider shouts abuse through the window, but she doesn't even appear to notice.

When we get back, she calls the police, and I can tell she's having trouble convincing them that this is serious. They ask to talk to me, and I have to explain again that yes, it was a false alarm last time but this time it definitely isn't.

'So,' the woman says, 'your sister has taken your little girl out without telling you where she was going, and you can't get through on her mobile, is that right?'

'Yes, that's right.'

'And they've been gone, how long?'

'I don't know. I was asleep, and when I woke up at ten to three, they were gone.'

'And it's now, what,' there's a pause, 'just coming up to five thirty. So they've been out a couple of hours.'

'No, it's longer than that. They must have been out for

ages because the kettle wasn't warm and there were only breakfast things in the dishwasher.' I'm speaking in a rush and I can tell it doesn't sound very convincing. 'And it's not just that.' I try to explain about Dusty and the flat; she agrees that it's odd behaviour but still doesn't see any reason to think that Anna has kidnapped Bonnie. 'So, she's left her key and not paid her rent. That's between her and her land-lord, frankly. Maybe she's gone flat hunting and taken your daughter with her?'

'No, no, she didn't want to move out. I think that's why she's taken her.'

The woman sighs. 'When were you expecting her back?'

'I *told* you,' I'm trying to keep my temper, trying not to cry, 'she didn't tell me she was going.'

'So she left the house without telling you?'

'*Yes*, I keep telling you, I was asleep.' My mum's hovering next to me, gesturing to take the phone again, but I shake my head. I need to do this myself.

'And you woke up at . . .' a pause '. . . approximately 14.50 this afternoon, is that correct?'

'Yes.'

'Afternoon nap, was it?'

I hesitate before answering. I can just imagine her reac-tion if I tell her I think Anna drugged my drink. 'No,' I say eventually. 'I was still asleep from the night before. I'd had a bad night.' I'll tell them about the sleeping tablets when I'm sure they're taking this seriously.

There's another long sigh, but then she says, 'All right,

we'll get someone to come round, but I can't guarantee it'll be straightaway.'

It's at this point that I finally lose control and start crying. 'Please,' I say between sobs, '*please* try to come as soon as you can.'

'Look,' the woman says, 'I understand that you're upset, but—'

At that point, my mum grabs the phone. 'Diana Mason here again. We understand you have other cases to deal with, but we have every reason to believe that my granddaughter may have been kidnapped by a young woman who, while she is a blood relation, appears to be more than a little unstable. All we're asking is that you give this case the priority it deserves, and if I suspect you are doing any less than that, be assured that I will discuss this with my MP, who, I might add, is a close personal friend and with whom I am in regular contact. Thank you.' She ends the call.

Then my mum does something I don't think she's done since I was about ten: she puts her arms round me and strokes my hair until I stop crying.

Simon has the decency to look shamefaced when he arrives. 'I'm sorry,' he mumbles at me when I let him in. 'But you can understand why—'

'Yeah, whatever. We're in the kitchen.'

My mother is noticeably cooler with Simon than usual. 'Right,' she says, pen in hand. 'The police can only act on what we tell them – if and when they eventually get here – so let's do some brainstorming. Just try to rack your brains for anything she's said in the past that could give us a clue as to where she might have gone. I don't suppose there's any chance at all this could just be another day at the seaside?'

'But why would she take all her clothes – or most of them, anyway.'

'She's taken all her clothes?' Simon looks surprised. 'You didn't tell me that.'

'I did. You weren't listening.'

'Yes, of course,' my mum says. 'Sorry, I'd forgotten that. So wherever she's gone, she's planning to stay at least for a while. But that doesn't necessarily mean she's gone for good, does it?' She looks from me to Simon and back again. 'I'm not trying to minimise this; I'm just thinking of all the possibilities. From what you've told me, it seems like Anna is genuinely fond of Bonnie.'

'Yes,' I agree. 'I don't think she'd do anything to hurt her. Although she does seem a bit . . .' I can hear the wobble in my voice. 'As you said, Mum, *unstable*.'

We all go quiet for a minute after I've said this. I don't *think* she'd do anything to hurt Bonnie, but again, I find myself thinking about those separated fathers who kill their children rather than let their partners have them.

'Do you think she's become too attached?' my mum asks.

'I'm not sure. Maybe. She does go on a lot about Bonnie and me being her only family. It's like she's been trying to play mummy. It annoyed me at first, because she seemed to be trying to take over, but she was so helpful, so supportive.'

I didn't intend this as a dig at Simon, but the way he shuffles in his seat, it seems that's how he's taken it. Well, tough shit. If the cap fits, Simon.

At that point, the landline rings and I dash into the sitting room to get it, heart racing despite the fact that I know Anna wouldn't call the landline. But it's just another one of those *have you had a car accident* calls. As I hang up, I hear my mum's phone ringing. 'Yes,' I hear her say, 'this is Diana Mason ... I see ... yes, I understand, and I appreciate your position. However, we have reason to believe the young woman who has taken my granddaughter may be mentally unstable.' There's a pause, and then, 'Please ensure that you do. Goodbye.'

She sighs as she puts her phone back on the table. 'That was the desk sergeant. There's been some sort of incident in Lewisham, apparently, and they don't have any officers available. She was most apologetic – genuinely, by the sounds of it – and assured me they'd send someone round as soon as possible, but she couldn't say when that would be.'

I sit down opposite Simon, but then stand up again immediately and start pacing. 'God, this is awful. We can't just sit here and do nothing.'

'We don't have much option,' he says.

My mum looks as if she's about to agree, then thinks better of it. 'Do you really have no idea at all where she might have gone?'

I think back over the many conversations I've had with Anna, wishing I'd paid more attention to the names and places she mentioned.

'Ooh, hang on,' my mum says, her face suddenly animated. 'I've an idea. Maybe we could track her phone. I saw this BBC drama recently – I can't remember what it was called, but—'

Simon's shaking his head. 'You have to install an app on the person's phone if you want to track their movements.'

'Well, they didn't on this programme, I can assure you. They just opened up a laptop, typed in the phone number – I think they had to pay with a credit card – and then it came up "tracking phone" and it showed on a map exactly where the phone was.'

Simon and I look at each other. 'Might be worth a look,' he says, reaching for my laptop. 'May I?'

I nod, sitting down again.

'Password?' he says as he opens it up.

'No password,' I say, and when he looks at me quizzically, I can't resist adding, 'I've got nothing to hide, so I never bothered setting one up.'

He sighs, and starts tapping the keys, then he stops to read the screen, and I see a flicker of hope in his eyes. 'Do you know what sort of phone she has?'

'What sort of phone?'

'Yes – iPhone or Android?'

'An iPhone, I think. Why?'

'Do we have her email address as well as her phone number?'

'Yes.' I read them out while he types them in, but then his face clouds over. 'Shit,' he mutters. 'I don't suppose you know her password?'

'I do, as it happens. I had to get into her phone for her once while she was driving – it's Bonnie123. I thought it was sweet at the time, but now I'm beginning to think—'

'Hang on,' he says, taking his wallet out of his back pocket. He takes out a debit card and types in the details, and a few seconds later, he punches the air. 'Yes!' he says. 'We're in.'

CHAPTER FORTY-SIX

Anna

I'm disappointed in you, Emily. That's my main thought as I drive through the night. All that *you can stay here as long as you like* stuff was bullshit, wasn't it? You didn't really want me with you. You just wanted to use me.

I don't know what I expected when I first started getting to know you, but it wasn't this. Oh, we were close for a while, when it suited you, but you dropped me pretty quickly when your old mate Zoe was around, didn't you? And now *mummy* wants to move in, you're dropping me again. You're my sister, for Christ's sake, my flesh and blood. I thought that meant something to you, but I'm beginning to wonder, I really am.

The last time you left me, it wasn't your fault. You were too little to do anything about it. But there's no excuse this time. After all those years we were apart, you should have wanted to make sure we were never separated again.

There's a little murmur from the back seat and I glance in

the rear-view mirror. Bonnie's finally asleep now, bless her. She must be dreaming.

When you were this age, you were as sweet and innocent as she is now. I loved you so much, from the moment they brought you home. They told me it was my special job to look after you, and I took that seriously. I did everything I could to protect you from anything nasty, from changing your nappy so you didn't get a sore bottom, to making sure you didn't fall off the roundabout in the park, to holding your ice-cream cone for you so that you didn't drop it. And then the day we had the crash, who was it who made sure you had enough to eat and drink, even though she was starving hungry herself? Who was it who got covered in cuts climbing out of the car window to go for help when you were trapped in your baby seat with your face pouring with blood and our dead parents in the front? Me, Emily, it was me, looking after you as always.

The only time I ever relaxed and let someone else take over was when we were with Gillian and Mike. And then look what happened. Off you went with the Masons to a better life. I'm not blaming you for that, not really. Although I bet you made yourself super cute so they'd want you all the more. But even if it wasn't your fault, the least you could do is be a bit more grateful now. I don't mean, *Ooh, thank you Anna, don't know what I'd do without you, Anna*. Because you obviously *do* know what you do without me, don't you? Otherwise, why would you be chucking me out so that bitch of an adoptive mother of yours can move in? I mean proper gratitude, like letting me be part of your life. And there's no reason not to, is there? Not now *he's* buggered off with someone else. Which you should have spotted coming a mile off.

I had a bit of a sleep before I left, but then I started to worry that you might wake up, even though with four Zopiclone in your system, it's highly unlikely. It's only taken two and a half hours to get here, and that's with a stop on the way. But I'm feeling tired now, so I pull into the coach and lorry park on the seafront. If I can get a couple of hours' kip before it gets light, I'll be able to think more clearly. Then I just need to wait until a reasonable time to turn up at Jess's.

I haven't decided what to do yet, other than see if I can stay with Jess for a while. At first, I only wanted to frighten you, make you suffer as punishment for the way you've treated me. See how *you* like it when someone you love is taken away. But Bonnie is my flesh and blood too, and as I've been driving, especially now I look at her precious little face as she sleeps in the back of the car, I can't think of a single reason why she shouldn't stay with me. She loves me, I love her, we should be together, like you and I should have been. She'll be better off with me, anyway. I don't have to work long hours, I hardly ever get pissed, and when you think about it, if she follows in your footsteps, another few years and she'll have forgotten about you completely.

As I drive through the town, there's a painful crick in my neck, and every time I move my head I get a stab of pain, each one reminding me that you've driven me to this, to running away in the night like some criminal when you know full well that I'm family. I should be welcome in your house.

At last, I turn into Jess's road. I pull up outside a massive detached Victorian house that looks as if it used to be posh but is now in a right state. There's dead ivy hanging off the side, big chunks of plaster missing off the front of the house, and one of the windows has an old blanket pinned up instead of a curtain. There are loads of wheelie bins lined up along the front wall, and two cars, a small van and two motorbikes parked in the front garden. From what I can see, it looks like there's more parking round the back, so I drive in and along the side of the house, parking behind another two motorbikes. I wonder how many flats there are in this house? Jess is at 27E. At least, I hope she is. We still send Christmas cards, but neither of us knows whether the other receives them. For all I know, she may have moved by now, although I think she'd have let me know. The last time we talked on the phone was after she wrote to tell me that Becky had died, but for some reason, I didn't put her number in my contacts. She put her email address in the card one year, but I forgot and threw the card away.

Bonnie's still sound asleep, and I pause to look at her before I wake her. I can see you in her, Emily. She looks just like you did at that age, those same fine blonde curls, the eyelashes that were so long they curved onto your cheek. Sweet and innocent, my baby sister.

'Come on, Emily, my darling,' I say as I undo her straps.

'Oops, I mean Bonnie.' She looks a bit confused when she wakes, but then she smiles at me.

There's a back door, I notice, but I can't see a bell so we walk round the front, climb the steps and ring the bell. I hold my breath. As I wait for her to answer, a massive seagull lands on one of the wheelie bins and screeches at me. When the door opens, I'm not sure it's her for a second, then I recognise the tattoo on her neck. 'Jess?'

She stares at me for a moment before she recognises me. Then she smiles. 'Anna! Oh my God! What the fuck are you doing here? And who's this?'

'My little girl.'

'You never said you had a kid.'

I shrug. 'Can I come in?'

''Course.'

I follow her up the stairs into a big, high-ceilinged room where a little boy of about five or six is watching TV. 'Turn that crap off, Archie, we've got visitors.'

The boy ignores her, so she grabs the remote and mutes the TV. 'Cup of tea, mate?'

'Yes, please,' I say.

'And what about this little one? What's her name?'

'Emily,' I say.

CHAPTER FORTY-SEVEN

Emily

Anna's phone is currently in Eastbourne, and now I think about it, I'm sure I remember her talking about someone who lived in Eastbourne. A friend. No, one of her foster sisters, I think. I look at the map on my phone; the blue dot isn't moving. 'Right.' I jump to my feet. 'I'm going down there.'

'Hang on, Em. Don't you think we should let the police handle this?'

'Are you serious? This is our *child*. They've already said they haven't got enough officers. They might not send anyone for ages yet. They might not send anyone until tomorrow.'

'That's true,' my mum says, 'but they're better equipped to find her. I know you're worried, darling, and rightly too, but should you be driving in this state? Why not wait until the police can—'

'Mum, she's in danger! Can't you see that? In fact, the more I think about it, the more I'm sure Anna's not well, mentally, I mean. I don't *think* she'd hurt Bonnie, but she's obsessed. She was obsessed with me, and now she's obsessed with Bonnie, and that could be dangerous.'

'All right,' Simon gets to his feet, 'Diana, could you stay here in case the police turn up?'

'Of course.'

Simon picks up his car keys. 'Come on,' he says, looking at me. 'I'll drive.'

'I know Anna better than you do. I need to be the one to talk to her.'

'You can talk to her, that's fine – I'm just saying I'll drive.'

For a moment, I consider climbing into the passenger seat next to him, and sitting there passively while he ponders the best route and then drives us to the coast like we're on some Sunday outing. I can't do it. 'No,' I say, 'I need to drive there myself.' My desperation to get to Bonnie is physical, the desire to move forward – to run, to fly if possible – feels like a yawning, gaping emptiness in my stomach. It's as though the umbilical cord has been pulling at the core of me and now, stretched to its limit, it'll snap if I don't close the gap between us. 'I'm going now.' I call over my shoulder as I grab my keys from the bowl by the front door.

As I glance back to say goodbye, I see his stricken face and I relent. Bonnie is his daughter, too, even though he walked out on her. On us.

'I don't really want to be in a car with you, Simon, but you can come if you want.' It occurs to me that it might be useful to have him there to keep an eye on the map. Just because Anna's phone isn't moving at the moment, doesn't mean it'll stay there in the time it takes us to drive from here to Eastbourne.

'Let's take my car,' he says as we get outside. 'It's faster.'

'Fine,' I say, walking round to the driver's side. 'Toss me the keys.'

'Oh come on, Em. Don't be silly, I'll drive.'

'Fuck you, Simon,' I say, going back to my car. I'm inside and have started the engine while Simon is still trying to argue with me. I click my seatbelt in place and start reversing out of the drive. 'Emily! For fuck's sake,' he shouts. 'Wait!'

'Three seconds,' I shout. 'Then I'm going.'

He wrenches open the passenger door and jumps in beside me.

I don't even notice the first twenty miles. Simon's keeping an eye on my phone so we can make sure she's still in the same place. He tries to talk at me, but all I manage is a few noncommittal noises to show that I've heard him, which I haven't, really, because I don't take in a word he's saying. Anna's not thinking straight, she's definitely unstable, and she has my child. I can't stop thinking about all those newspaper stories about fathers driving over cliffs or into lakes with their children in the car. What makes a man kill his own flesh and blood in such cases? Is it simply to get back at their partners, the ultimate punishment for the women who reject them? Or is it more a case of, *if I can't have the children, you're not having them either?* Is it grief triggered by what they perceive as the loss of their children, or is it pure revenge? I comfort myself with the thought that it's only disturbed men who do such terrible things; I've never heard of a woman doing anything like that. Although I suppose women are less likely to be separated from their children in the first place.

'You're doing eighty, you know.' Simon points out half-way down the A21. 'It's a seventy limit.'

'Oh, fuck off.'

'Christ's sake, Emily. I'm only bloody saying.'

I don't reply. I'm surprised at myself, really. I don't usually swear at him like that, even if he's pissing me off. I'm just aware that suddenly I couldn't care less whether I upset him or not. It's quite liberating. I do glance at the speedometer, though, and I'm going a *little* over the speed limit, but I'm not doing eighty. And anyway, this bit of the road is completely straight and there's not much traffic, so yeah, I'm driving a bit faster than I should so I can get to my baby.

He doesn't say anything else for the next hour, apart from confirming that the winking blue dot is still in the same place.

As we pass a sign saying we're just eight miles from Eastbourne, my stomach makes a loud growling noise and I realise I've not eaten anything at all for almost twenty-four hours. 'Can you see if . . .' but before I can finish the sentence, Simon opens the glove compartment.

'Yeah,' he says, 'there's a packet of Haribos, but that's all.'

'They'll do.'

He opens the pack and hands me a Strawb.

'Thanks.' I remember how cute I once thought it was that we often knew exactly what the other was about to say without them actually saying it. I put my hand out for another sweet. It doesn't seem all that cute anymore. Just obvious, really.

Eastbourne 5 miles, the sign says.

I'm aware of Simon shuffling in his seat, sitting up a bit straighter. I do the same as he passes me another Strawb. The atmosphere in the car has changed now we're here, and I guess we're both wondering what's going to happen when we come face to face with Anna.

My heart is clattering in my chest as the winking blue dot leads us to a huge detached house in a tree-lined road in what must have once been an affluent area but is now very run-down and shabby-looking. Either side of the front wall there are stone pillars where, presumably, the gates leading into and out of the front drive would once have been. I'm fairly sure now that Anna told me one of her foster sisters lived in a flat in Eastbourne. This must be it. There are quite a few vehicles already parked on the drive in front of the house, so I pull up in the road outside. We both get out of the car, even though I said I need to face Anna on my own. Bonnie's our child but Anna is my sister and it's me – and Bonnie – she's obsessed with. I don't have the energy to argue at the moment, though, so we both go through the entrance to the driveway. I can't see Anna's Skoda among the vehicles parked in front of the house, but Simon is still holding my phone, and the winking blue dot confirms we're very, very close. As we approach the house, I look down the side where there are more cars parked at the rear, and there it is, Anna's car – proof that she's here.

Simon goes up the steps of the front door. 'Bloody hell,' he says. 'There are about ten doorbells. Start from the top and work down, I guess.' He rings the top bell, and by the time I'm standing next to him, he's rung the next one, too. 'Wait!' I say, before he can press any more buttons. 'Look – there are names.'

Not every bell is labelled, but I read the ones that are, and when we get to J Banbury, I remember. 'That's it. Jessica Banbury – her foster sister, Jess.'

CHAPTER FORTY-EIGHT

Emily

I press the bell and we wait. Nothing. I try again, but there's still no response, either to my ring or to the two bells Simon pressed. Taking a step back, I look up at the windows, some bare, some with broken blinds or half-drawn curtains. There are no lights on, but it hasn't started to get dark yet, so that's not surprising. I press the bell again, keeping my finger on it this time.

'Emily.' Simon's still holding my phone. He shoves it in front of me. 'Look!'

I take it from him. For a second, I don't register that the winking blue dot is moving.

Then I hear the engine start.

'Fuck!' Simon shouts, and as I turn, he leaps back down the steps and runs towards Anna's car, which is coming around the side of the house.

'Anna!' I scream, running behind Simon who's just in front of me. Anna meets my eye, her face impassive, like stone. Bonnie doesn't look up because her attention is focused on the bag of crisps she's trying to open. 'Bonnie!' I scream, but I don't know if she hears me. Simon reaches the car first and he has his hand on the door, but now she's through the gap, Anna puts her foot down causing the gravel to spray up from her wheels as her car hurtles away from us, out of the driveway and into the road.

Simon's running after her, shouting and waving his arms. Does he really think that's going to make her turn the car around and come back? Idiot. 'Call the police!' I shout as I wrench open my driver door and throw my phone onto the passenger seat. I can only remember the first part of her registration number but I call this to Simon as I jump into my car and start the engine. He shouts at me to wait for him as I do the fastest three-point turn in history, missing a parked car by a millimetre. 'Sorry, I can't!' I call out of the window. His stricken expression causes a momentary tug at my heart-strings, but waiting would take precious seconds and I don't want to lose sight of Anna's car. 'Sorry,' I say again as I pull away, tyres screeching. I hope he knows I mean it.

She's driving quite fast and not indicating when she takes a corner, so I can't anticipate her next move. Where is she heading? And what's she planning to do? I'm trying to think like Anna. This all kicked off when she thought I was pushing her out, even though I wasn't. I'm not too far behind her, but she's taking so many corners, I think she's trying to shake me off. I'm starting to feel nauseous as I accelerate and brake, accelerate and brake. On the passenger seat next to me, my phone goes. I know without looking that it'll be Simon. Soon we're on the A road, picking up speed. It's a fifty limit along here but a quick glance at the speedo shows we're doing just over sixty. I'm closing the gap, and if I can overtake while there's room, hopefully I can force her to stop. But she's going even faster. I'm keeping up with her and the needle is now hovering over seventy. Just as I think I spot an opportunity to overtake, another car appears out of nowhere and pulls in front of me. 'Fuck,' I mutter. Anna's several metres ahead of the car in front. He's going fast, but not fast enough. 'Fuck!' I say again, banging my hand on the steering wheel in frustration. For a second, I think I've lost her as she disappears around a bend, but then I spot her up ahead where the road widens.

I put my foot down as soon as I'm able and overtake the other car, causing the driver to lean on the horn in outrage. I need to overtake her, then stop her from overtaking me. Without any warning, her car veers across the grassy verge of the central reservation and does a U-turn. Oh my God, what is she *doing*? I can't believe she's driving like this with Bonnie in the car. I take my foot off the accelerator and slow right down. There's no gap, nowhere for me to turn. Shit, shit, shit! What she's just done is crazy, but the fear that's growing inside me takes over. *Fuck it.* I check to make sure the road is clear, then I wrench the steering wheel as far as it'll go to the right and bounce over the central reservation after her, turning so that I'm following her again, back towards Eastbourne. I push my foot down a bit further and I see the speedometer nudge up to eighty. Just when I think I've lost her, I spot her rear lights up ahead. Then the speed limit changes and she slows down very slightly. For a few seconds, I cling to the hope that she's realised how stupid this is and that she's heading back to that house. My phone goes again. I ignore it. Then I hear sirens approaching. Simon must have given the police her details and somehow, they've found us. As the police cars get closer, Anna pulls over, and I feel the panic starting to subside. Thank God she's seen sense. But as the whole line of cars moves to the side, the two police cars whizz past, lights flashing and sirens fading into the distance.

The line of traffic starts to move again, with Anna at the front, about four cars ahead. 'Fuck!' Tears of frustration spring to my eyes as we set off again. If I can just keep her in sight . . . but then she turns off sharply without indicating, prompting several angry horn blasts from the cars immediately behind her. I hit my indicator and follow her. She's picked up speed now so I do the same, shortening the gap between us. She makes another turn, then another, and I'm struggling to keep up. I'm wondering where she can possibly be heading when I spot a road sign – *Beachy Head Road.* She's heading for the cliffs; Anna is heading for a world-famous suicide spot, and she has my daughter in the car.

I throw my body forward, putting every fibre of my energy into making this car move as fast as it can. The steering wheel presses into my chest. It's as though the car and my body are moving as one, forcing everything forward. My phone rings again and I want to hurl it out of the window, but I know I might need it to keep track of where she is. I know it's futile, but I press the horn in the hope of attracting her attention. 'For Christ's sake,' I mutter. 'Please, please stop.' There are two voices in my head, one telling me that although Anna is behaving erratically, she loves Bonnie and she wouldn't hurt her. But the other voice screams at me that she's mad, deranged; that she wants my daughter for herself and if she can't have her . . .

Anna seems to have slowed down and for a second I think she's going to pull over, but then I remember her telling me that her old Skoda struggles with hills. She's just a few metres ahead. Maybe I can use this opportunity to get in front of her and force her to stop. Shit. There was a sign back there and I missed it. What if it was a warning that we're near the clifftop? How far away are we? Half a mile? Less? Suddenly, I feel absolutely certain that Anna intends to drive off the cliff with Bonnie. I lean on the horn, I'm crying openly now, tears streaming down my face. It's clear up ahead so I flatten the accelerator to the floor, roaring past her and positioning myself in the middle of the road. I touch the brakes, wait half a second, then touch them again. I glance in the rear-view mirror and see her fall back slightly. For a split second I think it's working, but she speeds up again and tries to overtake. I move to the right to block her, but a second later, the front of her car looms in my nearside wing mirror as she tries to come up on the inside. What the hell is she doing? I steer to the left, forcing her to slow down, but again she tries to overtake. For a second, our eyes meet as the cars draw almost level; she's gripping the steering wheel and I can see the determination on her face. She's not going to give up. I accelerate again and manage to edge in front, holding the road as she drops back, but I know she'll try again. Just then I spot another sign – a car park, we must be nearing the clifftop. This is my last chance to stop her. The road ahead is still clear and as soon as I can see her in the rear-view mirror, I put my foot down once more. My car is more powerful than hers, and in no time I'm a good way ahead. When I'm sure that enough distance is between us, I wrench the steering wheel to the left on full lock as though I'm doing a three-point turn. I'm about to reverse so I can position the car across both lanes, when instead of slowing down, Anna seems to be speeding up. I scream, gripping the steering wheel. I see her face and it looks like she's screaming too, and I can't tell if it's in fear or anger. There's an excruciating screech of brakes. My body jolts as her car thuds into the side of mine with a sickening crunch, the metal grinding as the passenger door caves in and I'm shunted along the road. My airbag inflates, pinning me to the back of the seat as we come to a stop on the opposite side.

I sit there, dazed, as the silence settles around me. Time has slowed down and it takes a moment for me to register that it's over. Before I can register anything else, everything goes black.

EPILOGUE

The road is quiet and still, as though holding its breath. Now the cars are no longer moving, there is no sound but the whisper of a faint evening breeze as it ripples through the long grass lining the sides of the road.

Despite your momentary blackout, you are relatively unhurt apart from a whiplash injury that will cause you low level pain for many years to come. Your sister, alive but unconscious, isn't moving. There are no airbags fitted in her ancient car, so there was nothing to stop her head from slamming into the side window as her car ploughed into yours. On impact, her offside wing crumpled, concertina-like, the metal pushing its way into the soft flesh of her right leg. These injuries are serious enough, but the steering wheel thudded into her chest with such force that it caused a myocardial contusion, a bruise on the heart. It is this that threatens her life.

The sky over the English Channel is ablaze with reds and

pinks and yellows as the sun sinks down below the horizon, casting a golden glow over the water. In those few quiet seconds as you come round, your disorientation is such that you wonder briefly if you are waking from another of those car crash nightmares that have plagued you ever since you discovered the truth about your history. But then reality kicks in. Bonnie! As you open your door, the movement causes a sharp pain to shoot from your neck into your shoulder and up into your head. Bonnie, silenced briefly by shock, starts to scream. Adrenaline floods your system, masking the pain and allowing you to spring into action. You leap from your seat and run round to the undamaged side of Anna's car. *'Okay baby,'* you shout, *'it's all right, Mummy's here.'* You're sending up a silent prayer at the same time, *please let her be okay; please don't let her be hurt.* A faint recollection of that other long-ago car crash stirs deep within the chambers of your memory, the echoes resonating as you tear the door open, release the buckle on the car seat and pull your terrified daughter into your arms. 'All right, baby. It's okay, sweetheart, Mummy's here now.' Your child is hot and rigid with fear, but you can feel her little body starting to relax as you hold her close and stroke her hair. As her crying subsides, you check for any injury, examining her head, face, limbs. Miraculously, she seems unhurt.

As you walk back round the wrecked Skoda to get to your own car, you turn to look at Anna, her crumpled form crushed into the now-tiny space that was once the driver's seat. Her head is scrunched up against the driver door and there's a lot of blood. You can't see where it's coming from, but it's darkening her hair and pooling in her lap. You stand there, looking down at this woman. Your flesh and blood. You should probably call an ambulance – that's if it's not already too late – but then you consider what she's put you through, and what she's put your poor, terrified baby through.

What you can't know is that you were wrong when you assumed Anna planned to end her life and take Bonnie with her. She never intended to hurt Bonnie, because she loves the child – you were right about that. Her feelings for you are rather more complicated. They began as love, but then hate crept in. And there's a thin line, as they say. She only really wanted to scare you, but with the love and hate all jumbled up together in her heart – her poor, bruised heart – she wasn't thinking rationally and it all went too far.

And now it's up to you. Still murmuring reassurances to your precious child, you walk back to your badly dented car. Your phone has fallen into the footwell, but you should still be able to reach it. What with tracking Anna's phone, it's been working overtime today, so it may have died already, but if there's still some life left in the battery, you'll almost certainly call an ambulance.

Almost certainly.

ACKNOWLEDGEMENTS

The first round of thanks goes to the people who really make a book happen! My profound gratitude to my editors Clare Hey and Judith Long for their expertise and insightful feedback on various drafts. My thanks to Clare particularly for her feedback on the initial outline and partial draft – Clare is able to see what I'm trying to do, even when I can't see it clearly myself! Judith's skilful editing and astute feedback on later drafts really pulled the whole thing into shape and helped me to nail the ending. And, as always, I am indebted to my agent Kate Shaw, whose hard work and dedication knows no bounds. I know it's a bit of a cliché, but without Kate's encouragement (and a well-placed deadline or two) this book truly would not exist.

Massive thanks to the fabulous team at Simon & Schuster for all the extra work that goes on behind the scenes – from copyediting, proofreading and creating the *amazing* cover, to publicity, marketing and sales. Thank you all so much!

As part of my research, I did a lot of reading around the subject of children in the care system. Two books I found particularly helpful are Lemn Sissay's beautifully written and deeply affecting memoir *My Name is Why* and Kit De Waal's incredibly moving and equally well-written novel *My Name is Leon*. I highly recommend both these books, whether you have a particular interest in the care system or not. Can I also thank Joe Lumley and Eleanor Haworth of Adoption UK who gave up their valuable time and allowed me to pick their brains on various matters around care, fostering and adoption. Any remaining errors are my own.

I couldn't have written this book without the support of friends and writing buddies. My thanks as always to my very good friends, authors Russell Thomas and Marion 'Dill' Dillon. Not only did these two stalwart mates give me wonderfully perceptive feedback on almost everything I wrote (sometimes on several versions!) but they also kept my spirits up with coffee, cake, wine and gossip. Russ and Dill, without your friendship and encouragement, this book ... well, you know the rest.

My thanks also to Ruby Speechley, Iona Gunning and Sue Hughes for helpful plot chats, and to Ellie Phillips and Darren Brett for their perceptive and useful feedback on some of the earlier sections.

I also want to say a special thank you to readers, bloggers, reviewers and booksellers who are so supportive to authors. We would be lost without you – a story only becomes whole once it's being read. I love hearing from readers on Twitter,

Instagram, Facebook and through my website, so do get in touch.

Finally, as always, the greatest debt of all is to my husband, Francis, for his unwavering belief in me, for his support and encouragement, for the proofreading, the plot chats, the tea-making and the wine-pouring and, most of all, for the love and the laughs.

ABOUT THE AUTHOR

Susan Elliot Wright grew up in Lewisham in south-east London. Before becoming a full-time writer, she did a number of different jobs, including civil servant, cleaner, dishwasher, journalist and chef. She has an MA in writing from Sheffield Hallam University, where she is now an associate lecturer, and she lives in Sheffield with her husband.

To find out more,
visit her website: http:/www.susanelliotwright.co.uk
or follow her on Twitter @sewelliot.

Read on for an extract from

The Flight of Cornelia Blackwood
Susan Elliot Wright

**Everyone knows what Cornelia did all those years ago.
But no one knows what she will do next.**

Cornelia Blackwood lives a quiet life. When
she goes to the corner shop to buy milk,
people whisper behind her back.

Her one constant, her rock, is her husband. But when he
doesn't come home from a work conference, she is left
alone to try to pick up the pieces. And before long, the
secret he has hidden from her for all these years is laid bare.

Available in print, eBook and eAudio

SIMON &
SCHUSTER

CHAPTER ONE

NOW

I only open the back door for a moment to let the smoke out, but it is enough time for the creature to walk in, its black, claw-like feet clicking on the tiles. I grab a wooden spoon from the earthenware jar next to the hob and throw it at the crow, jolting my back and missing the crow by a mile. The bird flutters its feathers and caws twice at me before flying back outside. I slam the door shut, hands shaking as I turn the key in the lock, and as I toss the burnt toast in the bin, I realise my legs are trembling violently. I steady myself against the worktop and concentrate on my breathing until I feel calmer. It's not unusual for crows to be out there on the grass, or even for them to come up close to the house to peck around the plant pots looking for snails, but they've never tried to come inside before. Does this mean I can't ever leave the back door open again? My fingers twitch for a cigarette, but I promised myself I wouldn't smoke in the house when Adrian was home, and if I'm going to give up properly I need to stick to it. I can't resort to a cigarette every time something upsets me, or I'll be chain-smoking again in no time.

I start to get to my feet, but the pain makes me stop sharply mid-movement. When it's this bad I have to go back to using my stick, and I hate doing that – it makes me feel more like eighty than forty. Most of the time now I can manage without the bloody thing, but my back is really stiff today, probably because of all the sitting I did yesterday. Throwing that wooden spoon wasn't too clever – I'll probably be in pain for the rest of the day now. Leaning on the stick, I walk to the other side of the kitchen and switch on the coffee machine, but even that movement, reaching out and pressing the switch, sends a twinge down my spine, through my hip and into my leg. I should have been more careful yesterday – done my exercises at lunchtime, or at least taken a walk. The first tutorial was early so I'd hit the rush hour, which meant the drive into town took longer than usual, then three tutorials back-to-back before lunch and another two in the afternoon. But it's not often I have a day like that, and I'm grateful to the university for being so flexible. For having me back at all, really, after all that's happened.

I listen to the floorboards creaking overhead as Adrian moves around in the bedroom, packing for another conference. I hate waiting for him to leave the house. There's something about the sound of him preparing to go that makes me hyper-aware of his going, as if he's even more absent as he's getting ready than he'll be when he's gone.

The coffee machine whirs and clunks as I walk slowly to the kitchen door. 'Adrian?' I call up the stairs. 'You got time for coffee?' He can't hear me. I could go upstairs to ask him, but my back's killing me, and he'll probably want to get going anyway. I take my coffee into the sitting room and lower myself carefully into a chair by the window facing the garden. At least in here I can't hear him moving around so much. I light a cigarette and draw the toxins into my lungs, despising myself. Usually I open the door to the garden while I'm smoking, but that crow walking into the house completely freaked me out, so I leave it closed.

There's a breeze blowing up outside, and the trees in the woods beyond the fence are moving, the odd leaf floating to the ground. The leaves are beginning to change colour, and in a few weeks they'll fall from the trees, covering the grass in a carpet of russet, copper and gold. Start of the Autumn term. After two years of working solely on a one-to-one basis with final year students, returning to my old role is a bit scary. It's only a couple of days a week, and I can cope with the work-setting, marking, departmental meetings and awaydays, but the thought of standing up in front of a full lecture theatre ... Even the thought of being back in the department is daunting, but if my life is ever going to return to anywhere near normal I need to start interacting with people again. Mike, my line manager, has been great – really supportive. He tells me several times that colleagues will be pleased to see me back, but I'm not convinced.

I hear Adrian hurrying down the stairs, and then immediately bounding back up again. He's so heavy-footed when getting ready to go anywhere that my senses are on high alert, every nerve ending waiting for the next sound or movement. I squash out my cigarette. I *must* stop soon. He's been great about it, but he shouldn't have to put up with this. It was a stupid thing to start doing. I look at the pack on the coffee table, a plain white box with the words SMOKING KILLS in stark black letters. I wonder what my undergrads would think if they knew, given how I used to have a go at them when I came across little groups on campus, puffing away outside the library or the lecture theatres. *You've got away with it so far,* I'd say, *but what if you knew for sure that the next cigarette was the one that would trigger lung cancer? You'd stop, wouldn't you?* It was so straightforward. Who knew I'd end up relying on the bloody things to help get me from one hour to the next?

Adrian is coming down the stairs again. It sounds like he's lugging his suitcase this time. I take a swig of coffee. It's cold, but it'll tone down the taste of smoke on my lips when I kiss him goodbye. He appears in the doorway just as I reach it, laptop bag over his shoulder. He opens his arms and pulls me gently into them, his lips resting against my hair. We hold each other for a few seconds before he releases me. 'Bad timing, really, isn't it? If it was next week, you'd be back at work and too busy to notice being on your own.' He sweeps back my fringe. 'Will you be okay?'

'Yep – course I will.'

'How's your back?'

'Not too bad. I can take more painkillers soon, and when they've kicked in, I'll do my exercises.'

'Good. What will you do while I'm away?'

'Get ready for next week, I suppose. I've done all the reading, I just need to get my thoughts together. And I might start making some notes for the Hardy lecture.'

'Lecture? I thought you said you wouldn't be lecturing straight away?'

'No, I've got a few weeks, but it's such a long time since I've done it, I really, really need to be prepared. You know what they say.' We say it together. '"Fail to prepare, prepare to fail".'

'You'll be great. I know you're nervous, but at least you've been in and out for tutorials, so it's not like you'll be facing everyone for the first time.'

I haven't told him that I arranged the majority of my tutorials off-campus to avoid bumping into colleagues.

He kisses me on the lips and picks up his suitcase. 'And if it turns out to be too much, you can always go back to supervision only.'

I nod. 'Yes, true.'

'You just need to get that first seminar out of the way and you'll feel better.' He pauses, touches my face again. 'I know it's hard to move on, but somehow—'

'I know. Now go on, or you'll be late.'

'Sorry, I didn't mean to . . . you know.' He picks up his car keys. 'I'll phone you later.'

'Aren't you getting the train?'

'Yes, but I've left it too late to call a taxi. I'll leave the car near the station.'

'Why don't I drive you?'

No, he assures me, he's ready to go now so there's no point in me coming out. I won't argue. Driving can be difficult when my back's this bad.

'If you're sure. Go on, then,' I stand on tiptoe to kiss him. 'Get going. I'll talk to you tonight. Drive carefully.'

He closes the door and the empty house settles around me. I hate it when we're apart – always have. It's how I knew I loved him, right from the start.

What She Lost
Susan Elliot Wright

All families have their secrets.
But the truth will out . . .

Eleanor and her mother Marjorie have always had a
difficult relationship and have somehow just failed to
connect. Now Marjorie's memory is fading, and her
grip on the things she has kept hidden is beginning
to loosen. When she calls Eleanor to say, 'There's
something I have to tell you', Eleanor hopes this will
be the moment she learns the truth about the terrible
secret that has cast a shadow over both their lives.

But Marjorie's memory is failing fast and she can't
recall what she wanted to say. Eleanor knows time
is running out, and as she tries to gently uncover
the truth before it becomes lost inside her mother's
mind forever, she begins to discover what really
happened when she was a child – and why . . .

Available in print, eBook and eAudio

SIMON &
SCHUSTER

The Secrets We Left Behind
Susan Elliot Wright

It was a summer of love, and a summer of secrets ...

She has built a good life: a husband who adores her,
a daughter she is fiercely proud of, a home with warmth and
love at its heart. But things were not always so good, and the
truth is that she has done things she can never admit.

Then one evening a phone call comes out of the blue.
It is a voice from long ago, from a past that she has tried
so hard to hide. Scott knows who she really is and what
she has done. Now he is dying and he gives her an
ultimatum: either she tells the truth, or he will.

And so we are taken back to that long hot summer of
1976 to a house by the sea, where her story begins
and where the truth will be revealed ...

Available in print, eBook and eAudio

**SIMON &
SCHUSTER**

The Things We Never Said
Susan Elliot Wright

The past shapes us all. But what happens when it hides a secret that changes everything?

In 1964, Maggie wakes to find herself in a mental asylum, with no idea who she is or how she got there. Remnants of memories swirl in her mind – a familiar song, a storm, a moment of violence. Slowly, she begins to piece together the past and the events which brought her to this point.

In the present day, Jonathan is grieving after the loss of his father. Then a detective turns up on Jonathan's doorstep to question him about crimes he believes Jonathan's father may have committed long ago . . .

As the two stories interweave, the devastating truth long kept hidden must emerge, and both Maggie and Jonathan are forced to come to terms with the consequences of the shocking and tragic events of over forty years ago.

Available in print, eBook and eAudio

SIMON &
SCHUSTER